MIGRANTS AND MALARIA

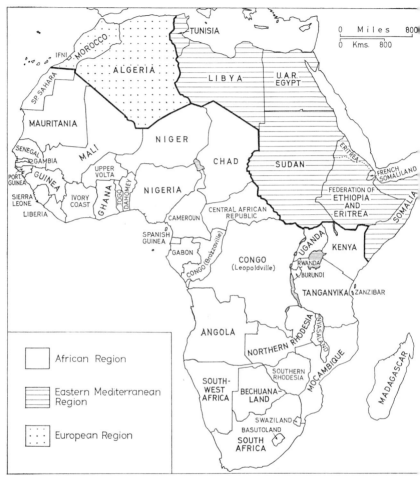

The countries of Africa and their allocation among three regions
of the World Health Organization.

R. Mansell Prothero

Senior Lecturer in Geography
University of Liverpool
Sometime Consultant to the
World Health Organization

MIGRANTS AND
MALARIA

Longmans

LONGMANS, GREEN AND CO LTD
48 Grosvenor Street, London W 1
*Associated companies, branches and representatives
throughout the world*

© *R. Mansell Prothero* 1965
First Published 1965

Printed in Great Britain by Richard Clay (*The Chaucer Press*), *Ltd.,
Bungay, Suffolk*

Foreword to the Series

THIS is the first of a new series of paperbacks, each of which will be written by a geographer. The emphasis in the series will be essentially on what geographers do, and on what geographers think. A concern with what geographers do is especially relevant to *Migrants and Malaria* which perhaps at first sight may seem an ill-assorted combination. In undertaking two consultantships to the World Health Organization, my colleague Dr. R. Mansell Prothero drew on his geographical training and knowledge and in doing so illustrated the contribution that geographers may make if they are given opportunities such as came his way.

Strabo, whom Macaulay once described as the Prince of Geographers, believed that one of the purposes of geography was to 'subserve the needs of States'. In similar vein Dr. Prothero suggests that geography can gain much by concerning itself with the practical affairs of life. As editor of this series I hope that these volumes may do something to indicate the relevance and application of geography to a variety of problems in different parts of the world and may demonstrate some of the work that geographers undertake, both in the field and in the library.

ROBERT W. STEEL

Department of Geography,
University of Liverpool.

v

Contents

Preface

IN the first chapter of this book I have outlined how, as a geographer, I came to be involved in planning for malaria eradication as a consultant to the World Health Organization. What follows is essentially a study in inter-disciplinary cooperation, and as an example of this I hope that it will be of interest to others besides medicals and geographers. For me an association with one of the specialized agencies of the United Nations has been of tremendous interest and value and I believe that I have been able to contribute something to one of the many major tasks which face the World Health Organization. Geography, I think, can gain much in influence by concerning itself with the practical affairs of life. I would not suggest that its only concern should be with these, but I feel that my own geographical studies are more worth while when they are so directed. Those geographers who share this view will understand how satisfying I have found my work with the World Health Organization.

I wish to acknowledge the help of many members of the World Health Organization concerned with malaria eradication, and I remember especially those working in remote parts of Africa, often under difficult conditions. My particular thanks go to Dr L. J. Bruce-Chwatt, Chief, Research and Technical Intelligence, Division of Malaria Eradication, W.H.O., Geneva, for his friendship and guidance and for reading and commenting on parts of the manuscript of this book. I also wish to thank Dr C. A. Alvarado, Director of the Division of Malaria Eradication, and Dr G. Gramiccia, Senior Malaria Adviser, European Region, W.H.O. However, the views expressed are my own and they do not represent the official views of the World Health Organization. Professor R. W. Steel and several of my colleagues in the Department of Geography of the University of Liverpool have assisted me in many ways; to the former and to the University of Liverpool I am grateful for leave of absence to work with the W.H.O.

Various ideas and information in this book have appeared in papers which I have published – particularly in the *Bulletin of the World Health Organization, Geographical Journal, Journal of Local Administration Overseas, Bulletin of the Inter-African Labour Institute, Africa,* and

ix

Pacific Viewpoint. I wish to make due acknowledgment to the editors of these journals.

I have not attempted to give the references to all the published and unpublished material upon which I have drawn. At the end of each chapter there is a brief bibliography of the more important works which may be consulted and from which further references may be obtained. Anyone writing on Africa at the present time is confronted with changes in the names of countries arising from political developments. Since the manuscript of this book went to the printers such changes have occurred in East- and South-central Africa. Nyasaland, Northern Rhodesia and Southern Rhodesia have become Malawi, Zambia and Rhodesia respectively, and there has been a union between Tanganyika and Zanzibar to form the Republic of Tanzania. The facts and figures used in this book all refer to the period before these changes took place, and so no attempt has been made to use the new names. To do so would only lead to confusion and to inconsistency.

The advice and skill of Mr A. G. Hodgkiss have been invaluable in preparing the maps. They were drawn by him and by Miss P. Joan Treasure in the Department of Geography of the University of Liverpool.

Neston
Cheshire

R. MANSELL PROTHERO

1 Migrants and Malaria; the Nature of the Relationship

SOME time ago the editor of the *Geographical Review* in the United States described her work over several decades as 'an adventure in serendipity'. To a geographer things that are unexpected rarely come as a surprise. Indeed, they are almost inevitable in a subject which sets out to examine relationships between widely varying phenomena as one of its tasks. Some of these relationships, to say the least, are unusual, others are esoteric and largely of academic interest. But there are many geographical phenomena, and relationships that exist between them and other phenomena, which are of importance in everyday life. It is with such relationships that this book is concerned. The realization of their significance came about largely by chance, but it opened up a new and vital field of work which is described here.

In the period 1954–55 an investigation was made of relationships between people and their land in Sokoto Province in north-western Nigeria, as part of a larger demographic study based on a recent census. This is an area where the population is increasing in a physical environment which offers only marginal possibilities for development, due largely to the low, variable and unreliable rainfall, which falls in a wet season that lasts for not more than five months. The fertility of the soil is rapidly depleted if unsatisfactory farming methods are used. As a result, population/land relationships, particularly in northern Sokoto, are beset with many problems of overpopulation and land hunger. Movements of a considerable proportion of the population are a major feature of these relationships and are a manifestation of these problems. They take place during each dry season which lasts from about the end of September until the following late April or early May.

Some of the movements are over only comparatively short distances (c. 30–40 miles) and people travel to trade, or to fish, or to find land which can be farmed by simple methods of irrigation, or even to fulfil social obligations. This is the time of year to visit relatives, to attend festivals or to make local religious pilgrimages. Similar movements occur in other parts of Northern Nigeria, and elsewhere in West Africa where there is a long dry season which reduces agricultural work, the basic economic activity, to a minimum. In Hausa, the language spoken by the majority of people in Northern Nigeria and in adjacent areas, and a *lingua franca* throughout West Africa, these dry-season migrants are known as *masu cin rani*, 'men who eat away the dry season'; by going elsewhere to work they help to conserve the limited supplies of food that are available in their home areas. In this way these movements help to alleviate some of the problems of overpopulation and seasonal food shortage.

There is also in each dry season a great exodus from Sokoto Province of men who travel long distances of 600 miles or more in each direction in search of work (Figure 1a and b). Similar seasonal movements of migrant labour take place from Mali, Haute Volta and Niger and from the northern parts of Ghana. The migrants travel on foot, and by road, rail and river, to areas where economic development is relatively advanced, in Senegal, Sierra Leone and Liberia and in the southern parts of Ivory Coast, Ghana and Nigeria. In all these areas there are demands for labour to augment the local supply.

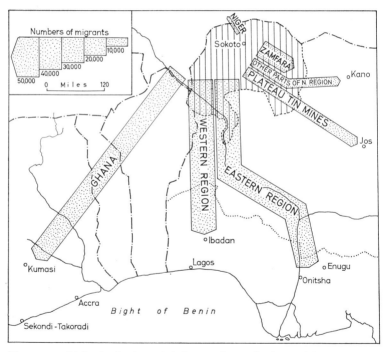

Figure 1a Main destinations and the numbers of migrant labourers from Sokoto Province, Northern Nigeria 1952–53. (Based on maps by the author published in *Africa* and *Geographical Journal*.)

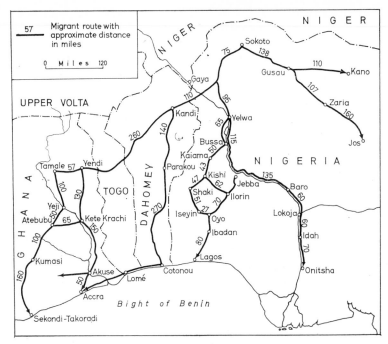

b Major routes travelled by migrant labourers from Sokoto Province. (Based on maps by the author in *Bulletin, World Health Organization*.)

In the study that was made of these migrations particular attention was paid to the volume and patterns of movement and to the physical and economic factors which influence them. Some attention was given to the implications and effects of labour migration, both on the home areas of the migrants and on the places where they go to work. The probable effects of the long journeys on the health of migrants were considered, and something was realized of the possibilities of the transmission of diseases through the uncontrolled movements of large numbers of people. Indeed, in May 1955 there was a minor outbreak of smallpox in Sokoto Province that coincided with the return from work of the majority of migrant labourers, and some of them were probably responsible for introducing the infection. However, no actual investigation was made of any of the health aspects of migration.

The importance and fuller implications of the movements of people in the transmission, control and eradication of disease became evident later when, in 1957, a report of the Sokoto study of labour migration was read and commented on by the Senior Malaria Specialist in

Nigeria.* He was then concerned with the organization of a project to control malaria in part of western Sokoto Province; the progress of this project was then and has subsequently been prejudiced by various types of population movement, both within the area of operations and between it and adjacent areas. Migrant labourers, when they return each year from working in and passing through malarious areas, bring fresh malaria infections and thus build up and maintain the reservoir of malaria transmission. The more localized movements that take place during the dry season make it difficult to locate people for administering various anti-malaria measures. There are also nomadic pastoralists within the project area who move throughout much of the year in search of pasture and water for their herds and flocks; these perhaps are the most difficult mobile element of all with which to deal. Their way of life and their natural reserve and conservative attitudes, which are characteristic of all pastoral peoples, make it difficult to integrate them into a malaria control programme. They thus tend to remain highly infected with the disease and are a menace as a reservoir of infection to those who might otherwise be made malaria-free.

In such circumstances the need to understand all aspects of population mobility is obvious. Furthermore, there is need to understand and to take into account many other facets of people's ways of life, for these are also relevant in the epidemiology of malaria and in planning for and promoting its eradication. The distribution as well as the movements of population, forms and patterns of settlement, types of dwellings and the materials of which they are constructed, occupations and social relationships and many other ordinary features of life are important and may be highly significant in their influence. Each of these, individually and in their relationships with one another, are studied within the field of human geography. The possibilities for interdisciplinary cooperation with those in the medical profession who are concerned with malaria and its eradication are clearly evident. Some of these possibilities have been realized during two periods that have been spent by the writer as a geographical consultant to the World Health Organization. On the first occasion in 1960, for a period of six months, population movements in relation to malaria eradication were investigated in Africa south of the Sahara, to assess the situation overall and to obtain some idea of the magnitude of the problems involved and of the data available. For two months in the summer of 1962, similar problems were investigated more intensively, this time north of the

* Dr L. J. Bruce-Chwatt, now Chief, Research and Technical Intelligence, Division of Malaria Eradication, World Health Organization, Geneva.

Sahara in Morocco. Upon these experiences, particularly, this book is based, but inevitably it also draws heavily upon the experience and investigations of others.

During the first consultantship extensive journeys were made by air and by road, beginning in Egypt and extending as far south as Southern Rhodesia, returning via the Congo (Brazzaville), Nigeria and Ghana. No detailed local investigations were possible, though there were fortunately several opportunities for gaining firsthand experience of problems in the field, particularly in Sudan, Ethiopia, Somalia, Tanganyika and Nigeria. In all the countries visited it was possible to consult with people possessing considerable local experience, and to learn a great deal from them. In Morocco, with more time available, closer acquaintance was possible in many parts of the country with the physical and the human factors that are likely to influence malaria eradication. During the Moroccan consultantship great use was made of the extensive documentation available, a legacy of the French influence in the country, and here also people with local knowledge were of great assistance.

While the emphasis in this book is upon the importance of human factors, and while malaria eradication is in many respects a human problem, there are obviously other factors which influence any malaria situation. Parasites, anopheles mosquitoes and men are essential components in the malaria complex. In the next chapter, therefore, this complex is outlined. Some indication is given of the nature of the disease, its significance in the past and at the present time, the means that are available for combating it, the extent to which they have been applied, the degree of success that has been achieved, and the hopes that are entertained for progress in the future. With this background the general aspects of population mobility and of other human factors are discussed, particularly for Africa, but with some reference to other malarious areas of the world. The remaining chapters are regional studies of the influences of human factors upon malaria and its eradication. Individual countries and groups of countries in Africa have been selected for these but no attempt has been made to survey all parts of the continent. Also, within the areas studied, the problems which are examined have been selected to give an indication of their variety, and no attempt has been made to achieve comprehensive treatment. For much of Africa there are not yet the data to make this possible.

BIBLIOGRAPHY

R. M. Prothero, 'Migratory Labour from North-western Nigeria', *Africa*, **27**, 1957, 251; *Migrant Labour from Sokoto Province, Northern Nigeria*, Government Printer, Kaduna, 1959; 'Some Observations on Desiccation in North-western Nigeria', *Erdkunde*, **16**, 1962, 111.

2 Malaria

MALARIA has been known as a major disease affecting mankind from very early times in recorded history, a disease which is debilitating in its effect on health and indirectly if not directly responsible for death. It has been claimed as one of the factors contributing to the downfall of the Roman Empire, when its incidence increased as a result of the neglect of drainage schemes and the consequent increased breeding of anopheles mosquitoes. Certainly, where it occurs in endemic form, malaria results in high mortality rates among young children in the early years of life. Those who survive this period then develop a degree of tolerance to malaria, though they are likely to experience recurrent mild attacks which seriously lower their resistance. Health generally suffers, and people are more susceptible to other diseases which may be directly the cause of death. Where malaria occurs in epidemic form, it may kill large numbers of people of all ages during an outbreak of comparatively short duration.

Parasites and mosquitoes

Malaria is caused by organisms which are referred to as malaria parasites. When they are present in the blood stream, these parasites will multiply, and attack and destroy the red blood corpuscles, thus causing grave physical debility. Several strains of the parasite exist and these are found individually or in combination in the various malarious areas of the world. The discovery of a parasite as the cause of malaria was not made until the second half of the nineteenth century when it was isolated by the Frenchman, Laveran, in the years 1878–80. His work revealed the fallacy of the long-held belief that miasmas, foul air rising from wet, marshy ground (hence the name 'mal aria' – 'bad air'), were the cause of the disease. Even with this major step forward in understanding the disease, another twenty years were to pass before Sir Ronald Ross, after his work in India and elsewhere, demonstrated that malaria was transmitted from one human being to another by female anopheline mosquitoes. After the mosquito has fed on the blood of an infected person the ingested parasites pass through a cycle of development before being passed on, by further feeding, to infect another individual. Establishing this basic relationship between parasite, host, vector and victim was of vital importance in understanding malaria (Figure 2).

Provided there are sources of infection, malaria may occur if there are suitable mosquito vectors to transmit it, and these may be found in areas where summer temperatures do not fall below 60° F (15·5° C) and where moisture conditions are favourable. Mosquitoes are unable to survive low temperatures, and thus the ameliorating influence of altitude on temperature may result in malaria-free areas occurring in latitudes where the disease is otherwise prevalent. There are many different species of mosquito which breed in different environmental conditions; the females of over sixty species are recognized as vectors of

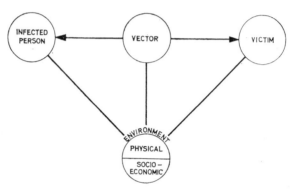

Figure 2 The relationships in malaria between infected person – vector – victim, each of which is influenced by factors in the physical and human (socio-economic) environment.
(The idea for this diagram came from a much more detailed one by L. J. Bruce-Chwatt.)

human malaria and the majority of these species thrive where temperatures are high and where there is adequate water in which to breed. *Anopheles gambiae*, the main vector of malaria in tropical Africa, breeds under conditions of heavy rainfall which are common, at least seasonally, over large areas of the continent. In many parts of Africa during the dry season, when conditions are either unfavourable or less favourable for *A. gambiae*, it may be replaced as the vector of malaria by *A. funestus* which does not breed in large numbers during the season of heavy rainfall.

At the end of the dry season when the onset of the rains provides greatly increased amounts of water, an explosive increase in mosquito-breeding usually occurs, with consequent increase in the rates of malaria transmission. The seasonal peak of malaria infection is thus likely to be related to both the amount and the distribution of rainfall. In areas with low rainfall and a long dry season, where water naturally is very scarce and conditions for mosquito-breeding are consequently very limited, the situation may be radically altered by the development of irrigation projects and the introduction of water from other sources. The construction of a network of major and minor water channels may provide ideal conditions for vector breeding, and malaria transmission may develop unless adequate measures are taken to prevent it.

The distribution of malaria (Figure 3a and b)

The distribution of malaria was much more widespread in the past than at the present day, and during the present century there has been progressive reduction in the areas which are affected by the disease. Nowadays it is found very largely in the tropical, sub-tropical and warm temperate regions, affecting more than one-third of the total population of the world. This distribution has produced a common misconception among many people, particularly in the temperate lands of western Europe and North America, that malaria is a disease only of the tropics and that it is associated with the 'underdeveloped' lands of the world. Truly malaria is nowadays a major public health problem in Africa, the Indian sub-continent, South-east Asia, the islands of the Pacific and tropical Latin America, but it still occurs in limited amounts in some parts of southern Europe. It was finally stamped out in Britain only in the early decades of this century and was not eradicated from the Netherlands until the 1930s. The agues and fevers suffered in parts of Britain up to the end of the nineteenth century were frequently malarial in character. Within the last decade the possibilities of renewed outbreaks of malaria, in places from which the disease had been eradicated, have been demonstrated in the United States. Outbreaks there were caused by the return of infected American servicemen from Korea to areas where there were anopheles mosquitoes to transmit the disease.

The present-day distribution of malaria shows very clearly its dominant occurrence in the tropics. In temperate and polar areas, for the most part, it has never existed, or has disappeared, or has been eradicated. There are important exceptions to this general pattern, in the northward extension of malaria into temperate latitudes in parts of the Far East and in its absence from the arid interiors of Saharan Africa, Arabia, Central Asia and Australia, from the high Andes in tropical Latin America and from other zones of high altitude in the tropics. With these exceptions, malaria is now a problem of the tropics and sub-tropics, affecting parts of the world where some of the highest concentrations of population occur. The table on page 12 shows, for

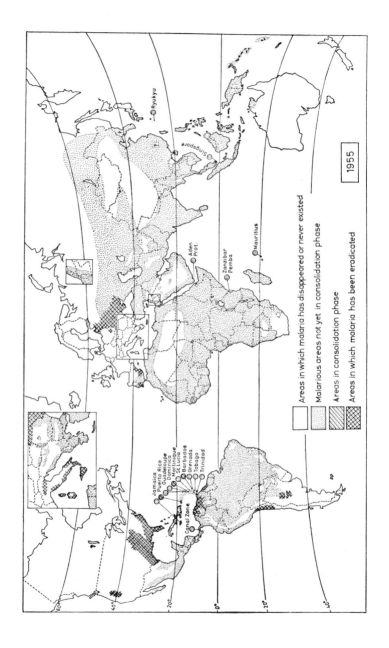

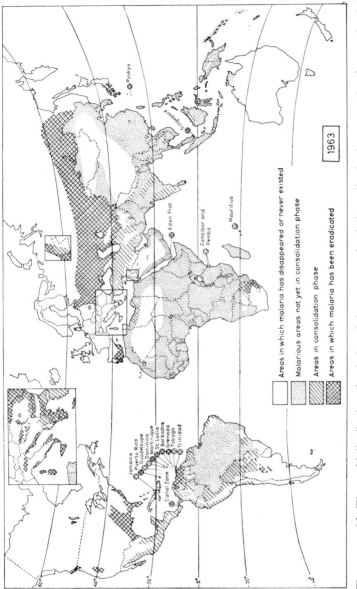

Figure 3a and b The world distribution of malaria and the progress of malaria eradication in 1955, and as forecast for the end of 1963. (Based on maps prepared by the Division of Malaria Eradication World Health Organization.)

example, the striking contrasts in the malaria situation in the adjacent continents of Africa and Europe.

Table 1 Malaria eradication in the continents of Africa and Europe on 31 December 1962

Continent	Population (ooos)				
	Where malaria was never indigenous, or disappeared without specific antimalaria measures	In original malarious areas	Where malaria eradication is claimed	Where malaria eradication programmes are in progress	Where malaria eradication programmes are not yet started
Africa	33,021	201,686	3,348	2,621	195,717
Europe	375,824	80,646	33,563	42,083	—

Source: Report on the Development of Malaria Eradication Programmes, Sixteenth World Health Assembly, Geneva, 1963.

These contrasts are in part a reflection of the physical conditions, which overall are more favourable to malaria in Africa than they are in Europe, but they also indicate the association of malaria, and its continued existence at the present day, with other factors. In Europe malaria has disappeared from those countries which are socially and economically most advanced; it is still found, in ever-decreasing amounts in small residual pockets, in those countries of southern Europe which are less well-developed. In 1963 fewer than two hundred cases of malaria occurred in Europe (excluding the U.S.S.R.) and some of these were imported from other parts of the world. Apart from the deserts, the part of Africa that is almost completely malaria-free is the Republic of South Africa, which is economically and in some other respects more advanced than other parts. These correlations are not without significance, for malaria like most diseases thrives under conditions of poverty, low standards of living, malnutrition, illiteracy and ignorance. But not only is it a result of these conditions, it also contributes both directly and indirectly to them. Low standards of living mean that health and education services are poorly developed and inadequate; under-nutrition and malnutrition cause debility and increase susceptibility to disease. A high incidence of disease results in further debilitation, which decreases efficiency and output at all levels, with resultant low standards of living. From this vicious circle in which they find themselves the malarious countries of Africa, Latin America and Asia, are now trying to break free. They are striving to advance all aspects of economic and social development, but the plans for the eradication of malaria and other diseases (sleeping sickness, yaws, schistosomiasis, bilharzia, trachoma and others) play an essential part in schemes for future improvement.

Malaria in Africa (Figure 4)

Malaria in Africa varies in nature and in intensity between the different parts of the continent. In low latitudes near the Equator (approximately

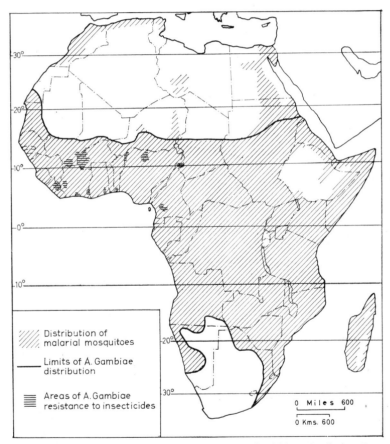

Figure 4 The distribution of malarial mosquitoes in Africa, the limits of *A. gambiae* and areas where vectors have shown resistance to residual insecticides. (Based on maps prepared by the Division of Malaria Eradication, World Health Organization.)

10° N to 10° S) conditions are favourable for the mosquito vectors to breed throughout the year, and with a large reservoir of infection in the human population there is perennial transmission of the disease. In the zones 10–20° N and S with lower rainfall, which is more variable and unreliable in amount and incidence, more confined in its season of fall and with a long dry season with low humidities, vector breeding is inhibited. Though there is a considerable reservoir of infection in these zones seasonal transmission of the disease is more pronounced, and there are marked peaks and troughs in the incidence of malaria from one part of the year to another. But between the Equator and latitude 20° N and S there is no clear natural break in transmission at any time of the year and malaria exists in endemic form though with variations in the degree of endemicity.

Over most of West Africa south of the Sahara, and over much of the basin of the Congo and its tributaries malaria conditions are classified as holo- or hyperendemic. Areas of high altitude on the eastern side of the continent are malaria-free – above 6,500 feet on the Ethiopian plateau, 6,000 feet in the Kenya Highlands and 5,000 feet in southern Tanganyika. In Rwanda and Burundi, at over 5,000 feet above sea-level, the incidence of malaria is only slight. At lower altitudes conditions are markedly different. Below 3,500 feet in Ethiopia malaria is hyperendemic and serious epidemics may occur above this altitude. Farther east, in the Horn of Africa, where the rainfall is low and in many parts less than ten inches per annum, endemic malaria occurs only near the rivers. These do not flow perennially, but sufficient water remains in isolated pools in the stream beds in the dry season for vector breeding and transmission to continue. Elsewhere in North-east Africa there is an annual discontinuity in the transmission of malaria, and the outbreaks of the disease which occur when the rains begin, and the number of vectors increases, are in epidemic form. The most recent serious epidemic occurred in the south of the Republic of Somalia in 1961, following excessive rainfall and flooding which came after a long period of drought. Hyperendemic conditions prevail in the low-lying lands along the east coast of Tanganyika and southward in Moçambique, and they extend inland up the valleys of the Zambezi and Shire rivers at altitudes mostly below 2,000 feet. Inland above 4,000 feet, and particularly on the High Veldt in Southern Rhodesia, conditions are relatively malaria-free.

Roughly north and south of the twentieth parallels of latitude the malaria situation changes from the conditions found within the tropical and equatorial zones. Only relatively small malarious areas remain in the Republic of South Africa and these are at low altitudes along the humid north-eastern coastal strip. Conditions are too dry in the Kalahari and other desert areas for mosquitoes to breed. In the great arid zone of the Sahara, Libyan and Egyptian deserts the disease is found only in scattered pockets in the oases, but it occurs on a very much greater scale in the Nile valleys in Egypt and in the Sudan. Elsewhere in North Africa malaria has, for the most part, a distinct seasonal pattern of occurrence, dependent on rainfall and the resultant water conditions. At high altitudes in the Atlas and other mountain ranges of the Maghreb the low winter temperatures prevent mosquito-breeding and malaria is virtually absent.

Attitudes to malaria

Where malaria occurs in epidemic form, with periodic or occasional sharp increases in morbidity and mortality due to the disease, its effects are spectacular and impressive. People in Africa and elsewhere who are subject to malaria at high levels of endemicity, learn, so to speak, to live with the disease; they are continually in contact with malaria and suffer from frequent infections. But, it must be remembered, these are the people who have managed to survive the direct and indirect effects of malaria in the earliest years of life. From 0–2 years of age mortality rates may be as high as fifty per cent, with deaths caused directly by malarial infections. Susceptibility at birth is universal, there is no inherited tolerance to the disease, racial immunity is non-existent; up to the age of 5 years the disease may be fatal. Those who survive beyond this age acquire a degree of tolerance; they are subject to periodic infections that manifest themselves in low fevers which are debilitating but not necessarily incapacitating. Deaths do not result directly from malaria, but periodic attacks may lower people's resistance to such an extent that other diseases which they acquire may prove fatal.

Under these circumstances people come to accept malaria as a part of life; among many illiterate communities it is scarcely even recognized as a disease. Mosquitoes may be regarded as a curse, not because they are vectors of malaria but because of their unpleasant biting habits. Endemic malaria is insidious in the ways it manifests itself and in its effects on people, and it is frequently difficult to convince those who are affected by it of the need for measures to control the disease or to eradicate it altogether. This is one of the many human problems that has to be faced in the battle against malaria in Africa and in similar areas elsewhere. While the means for successful eradication are available, major difficulties arise in the application of measures to bring this about.

Malaria control and eradication

From the time that the relationship between parasite–vector–host was understood it was possible to begin devising ways of dealing with malaria, either by attacking the parasite in man or by killing the mosquito vector.

Many effective drugs have been discovered, both to cure those who are suffering from malaria and to give protection and to prevent it being contracted. Chemotherapy and chemoprophylaxis, however, have to be considered in relation to the very large numbers of people who are infected with malaria or who are liable to infection in countries which, almost without exception, have poorly developed medical and health services. Large proportions of these populations have only very remote contact, and some none whatsoever, with medical facilities of any kind. Drug distribution and administration present major problems and to these must be added the high cost of drugs, which is a major drawback to their use on a large scale in poor countries.

The curative drugs do little to prevent further infection. Persons who are cured by them, but who may then be bitten again by infected mosquitoes will succumb once more to malaria. They may again be cured, but the whole process will be repeated subsequently unless they take a protective drug. The problems of the cost and distribution of protective drugs are magnified by the fact that there is not yet one that will give protection against the disease for any length of time. The drugs available must be taken daily, weekly, or at most every two weeks. It is not yet possible, as for example with yellow fever inoculation or smallpox vaccination, to provide protection for periods of several years. The absence of a drug with long-lasting effective protection is obviously a major drawback in the fight against malaria. Even in relatively small groups of people, over which it is possible to maintain fairly close control, the distribution of anti-malaria prophylactics, to ensure that they are taken regularly and comprehensively, has not yet been achieved with outstanding success. With larger groups, within which or between which there may be considerable mobility, it is impossible; and in any case the cost of the drugs would be prohibitive.

The alternative line of attack against malaria, and the one that has been developed over many years, is directed against the mosquito vector which is responsible for transmitting the disease. Sir Ronald Ross recommended 'mosquito reduction' in order to cut down the amount of transmission of malaria from infected to non-infected persons. If, by reducing the number of vectors, the rates of transmission can be brought down to very low levels, and this situation can be maintained for several years, then malaria will die out naturally in a population. Then, even if the mosquito population increases to its former numbers, it will not be a menace to health provided that no fresh reservoir of infection is introduced (Figure 5).

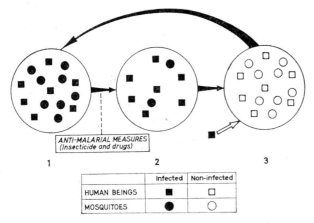

ANTI-MALARIAL MEASURES
(Insecticide and drugs)

	Infected	Non-infected
HUMAN BEINGS	■	□
MOSQUITOES	●	○

Figure 5 The effect of malaria eradication measures upon a malarious area.
Stage 1   A malarious area with infected human beings and infected vectors.
Stage 2   With the introduction of eradication measures there is a consequent reduction in the number of infected mosquitoes.
Stage 3   Following the success of eradication measures infections are stamped out in the human population, and though the number of vectors increases they present no menace provided there are no fresh sources of infection. But if one is introduced and measures are not taken to deal with it, it would be possible in time to return to the situation in Stage 1.

The early measures devised against the anopheles mosquito were directed to its breeding places. Extensive drainage schemes, undertaken in areas of swamp and marsh, had considerable effects on lowering the vector population and thereby the rates of malaria transmission. In addition, chemicals were used to destroy the mosquito in its inactive larval stage. Using these two methods of attack – drainage and larvicides – the successful eradication of malaria and of yellow fever was achieved in Cuba and Panama during the first decade of this century. Subsequently, insecticides were developed to deal with the mosquito in its adult stage, with the advantage that the cost of these was about a third of the cost of larvicides to apply and with the possibilities of them being much more effective.

During the Second World War, with fighting in many tropical areas of the world, there were important advances in the production both of anti-malarial drugs and of residual insecticides. Of the latter, D.D.T., B.H.C. and dieldrin are the main ones in use. The main feature of these insecticides is that they remain toxic to mosquitoes for long periods, under some conditions for six months or more after they have been applied. These residual effects have made possible the application of new techniques to reduce vector populations, which have been developed in accordance with vector habits. Many of the species of mosquitoes which transmit malaria are very largely both *anthropophilic* and *endophilic* – that is to say, they take their blood meals from human beings and they tend to rest indoors after biting. Given these circumstances and the availability of insecticides with residual toxic effects, it was demonstrated that a high percentage kill of mosquitoes could be obtained by thoroughly spraying with insecticides the inside surfaces of buildings occupied by human beings.

It has been shown that the long residual effectiveness of insecticides is dependent on favourable conditions and that these are very rarely experienced. Many of the surfaces on to which the insecticides are sprayed do not retain them satisfactorily. Most mud surfaces, for example, are highly absorbent, while the insecticide may not cling to reed or grass thatch, or to leaves. On any of these materials the toxic effects are soon lost. Frequently it is also necessary to renew annually the walls and roofs of houses by replastering and with new thatching. If these repairs take place shortly after spraying then the effect of the insecticide is immediately lost altogether.

In spite of these and other difficulties, spraying with residual insecticides in many malarious areas has killed sufficient mosquitoes to reduce malaria transmission appreciably, and so has lessened it as a menace to public health. In these circumstances control of malaria is established, but this situation can be maintained only by continued efforts since some vectors and also some sources of infection remain. Though these may be in relatively small numbers and at relatively restricted levels, both would increase again if spraying were to be relaxed. The maintenance of malaria control thus requires a continued drain upon resources for an indefinite period.

The World Health Organization and malaria eradication

Immediately after it was established as a specialized agency of the United Nations Organization in 1948 the World Health Organization became involved in the fight against malaria, as part of its task to promote and assist in measures for the improvement of public health throughout the world. Acting in a coordinating and advisory capacity, by stimulating and financing research work and by assisting in the collection and dissemination of information, the W.H.O. soon began to play a major role in malaria work. Various new strategies for malaria control were developed, involving particularly the use of residual insecticides, and to test these both pilot projects and major schemes for malaria control were established. Then, during the early years of the 1950s, experience gained in these schemes began to show the need for a fundamental change in approach. Not only were there the problems of having to spray indefinitely to maintain malaria control, but much more disturbing and ominous were reports from different parts of the world that vectors were becoming resistant to insecticides. The first instance was reported from Greece where the mosquitoes developed resistance to D.D.T. Cases of resistance have followed no logical pattern of particular species being resistant to particular insecticides. While, for example, *A. gambiae* has displayed resistance to dieldrin in some parts of West Africa, this has not been so with the same species and the same insecticide in other parts of the continent (Figure 4). Resistance is generally of two types; either the mosquitoes develop a genetic resistance or else it is of a behaviouristic kind. With the latter, vectors change their habits; because of irritation from insecticide they may avoid resting on surfaces that have been sprayed and may cease their endophilic habits and become exophilic and rest out-of-doors. With such changes, and particularly with the dangers inherent in the possibility of insecticide resistance building up on a massive scale, proposals were made for changing the whole strategy of malaria work – from control to total eradication of the disease.

The concept of malaria eradication is based upon reducing the vector population to such an extent that transmission of the disease ceases and all sources of infection are eliminated. Then, if this situation can be maintained over a number of years without the introduction of fresh infections, malaria will die out naturally in the population. This process may be assisted and speeded up by the use of curative drugs. These are the requirements in their simplest form, in detail the theory and practice of malaria eradication are most complex.

If this new approach was to succeed then it had to be made on a global scale and measures for eradication had to be introduced in all malarious areas. The decisions to adopt this approach, and that it should be promoted by the W.H.O., were taken by the representatives of the member-nations of the Organization meeting at the Eighth World Health Assembly in Mexico in 1955. To implement these decisions and to organize the work within the W.H.O., a Division of

Malaria Eradication was established at the Organization's headquarters in Geneva. A special fund (the Malaria Eradication Special Account) was inaugurated to finance the work. Since it was established the major contributions to this fund have come from the U.S.A.

In present circumstances the mounting of a global campaign against malaria, on an intensive scale simultaneously in all malarious areas, is impossible. Malaria eradication demands trained personnel, equipment and other materials in large quantities. These are all expensive, and men, materials and money are unfortunately least available in those countries where the needs are greatest. Here is a further aspect of the malaria–poverty–underdevelopment relationship. The major areas of the world in which malaria eradication has been achieved are those with relatively advanced economic development and thus able to bear the cost in both human and material terms. It is also significant that malaria eradication has been achieved on the largest scale in the U.S.S.R. where the controls that can be exercised by a totalitarian régime undoubtedly have played an important part in making success possible.

In the majority of the malarious countries applying the concept of eradication, it was possible in the early stages to launch only pilot projects in limited areas and covering only a small proportion of the total population. Though small in scale these pilot schemes illustrated the exact nature of the problems that were involved and that had to be solved in order to achieve malaria eradication. They also provided the means for finding out the most economical, effective and speedy measures for eradication. Problems arose concerning the parasite, the vector and the host, and the complex relationships existing between these three. One problem of major importance, which was demonstrated in many of the pilot projects and which is of direct relevance to the theme of this book, was of working in a limited area which cannot be secured and insulated from the areas adjacent to it. In these circumstances infected persons, and possibly even infected mosquitoes, may come into the project area from outside, or else elements of the population of the project area may go to adjacent malarious areas and return with infections.

As experience has accumulated so the approach to malaria eradication, and the methods employed have been modified. The strategy of eradication is now based upon four phases of operation – *preparatory, attack, consolidation* and *maintenance* (Figure 6). In the *preparatory* phase all the aspects of the malaria situation are assessed by pre-eradication surveys, and the resources for the attack are built up, particularly the training of personnel and the integration of the malaria eradication programme with the general public health infrastructure of the country or region concerned. In the *attack* phase, which may last a number of years, the aim is to interrupt malaria transmission by the application of residual insecticides, possibly supplemented by the use of drugs. When it has been shown that interruption of transmission is being maintained the programme enters the phase of *consolidation*. All methods of attack have then come to an end and close surveillance is of

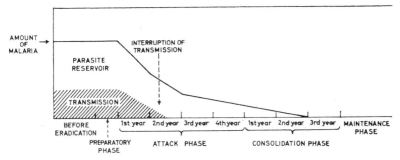

Figure 6 Phases in a malaria eradication programme, giving an indication of the timetable envisaged. (Based on a diagram in *Terminology of Malaria and of Malaria Eradication*, W.H.O., 1963.)

the utmost importance, in order to detect and to deal with any fresh outbreaks of malaria that may occur. If there are any outbreaks these will be localized and there should be machinery available to limit them and to deal with them quickly and effectively. The programme finally moves into the *maintenance* phase in which continued watch must be kept against the reintroduction of malaria.

Malaria eradication in 1962

At the end of 1962 out of a total population of 1,472 million living in the malarious, or formerly malarious, areas of the world, 329 million (*c.* twenty-two per cent) were living in areas from which the disease had been eradicated. A further 738 million (*c.* fifty per cent) were living in areas with malaria eradication programmes at various stages of development. The following table gives the position in each of the six regions of the world on which the work of the W.H.O. is based and Figures 3a and b allow a comparison of the world malaria situation in 1955 with that forecast for the end of 1963.

In the Americas every country with malaria now has an eradication programme. Besides the U.S.A., eradication has been achieved in a

Table 2 Malaria eradication in the W.H.O. Regions on 31 December 1962

	Population (000s)					
Region	Total	Where malaria was never indigenous, or disappeared without specific antimalaria measures	In original malarious areas	Where malaria is eradication claimed	Where malaria eradication programmes are in progress	Where malaria eradication programmes are not yet started
Africa	172,434	14,815	157,619	3,278	2,590	151,751
America	429,726	275,835	153,891	59,326	93,575	990
South-east Asia	634,678	35,238	599,440	1,467	552,279	45,694
Europe	698,861	391,937	306,924	245,744	43,013	18,167
Eastern Mediterranean	212,546	36,419	176,127	1,844	37,268	136,975
Western Pacific	215,573	137,120	78,453	17,367	8,855	52,231

Note: the populations of the Chinese mainland, North Korea and North Vietnam (total, 910,685,000) are not included.
Source: Report on the Development of Malaria Eradication Programmes. Sixteenth World Health Assembly, Geneva, 1963.

large part of Venezuela and in some of the West Indian islands. Most of South-east Asia is covered by eradication programmes, including that for India. The latter is the largest single scheme in the world; it was started in 1958 and covers 424 million people. Pakistan began its programme for malaria eradication two years later than India, while Ceylon is approaching the stage when the possibility of total eradication is very near. On the continent of Europe only a few small areas in Albania, Rumania and Yugoslavia remain in the attack phase; in the greater part of these countries, and in Greece, the consolidation phase is in progress and elsewhere total eradication has been achieved.

Malaria eradication in Africa presents the least favourable picture of any of the continents. Only in the Republic of South Africa is eradication nearly complete. There is a small area in Southern Rhodesia under the consolidation phase, but elsewhere the attack phase has only been initiated in Swaziland and the islands of Zanzibar and Pemba. Pre-eradication surveys are in progress in the Sudan and in Somalia, but in other African countries only comparatively fragmentary information is available on the malaria situation and on the factors which influence it. Most of this information has been obtained from pilot projects carried out only in limited areas. Remembering the extent of Africa, the variety of conditions found there, and the way that these frequently change over very short distances, it is probable that much of the data on malaria is not generally applicable. In three pilot schemes in Liberia, Cameroon and Uganda, the interruption of malaria transmission has been shown to be technically possible, but the problems of malaria eradication for the whole of Africa remain of monster proportions.

Size, distance and other less obvious difficulties inherent in the physical environment contribute to these problems. *A. gambiae*, the major vector species in Africa, is a particularly tough specimen with which to have to deal, and it has developed resistance to insecticides in a number of widely scattered areas. But from the experience gained in pilot projects, and from other investigations, it is clear that a very wide range of human factors contribute to the maintenance of high levels of malaria infection, and that they frustrate attempts to deal with the disease and bedevil the eradication programmes which are either in progress or which are in the process of being developed.

This statement is not meant to belittle in any way the importance of malaria parasites or mosquito vectors. But it is clear that while the technical measures (drugs and residual insecticides) are available for dealing with parasites and mosquitoes, major difficulties arise in the general contexts in which these measures have to be applied. It is no exaggeration to say that human beings most markedly prejudice the development and application of schemes for successful malaria eradication. The chapters which follow are concerned with illustrating these human problems and with demonstrating the need for applying geographical considerations, particularly within the field of human geography, to them. These considerations involve human beings in their relationships with one another and with the environment in which they live and of which they are part.

Parasites and vectors can be subjected to laboratory experiments and may be expected to behave according to principles which can be determined with a fair degree of certainty. Unlike parasites and vectors, people cannot be experimented with under laboratory conditions and, because of their infinite variety and inherent lack of logical response and behaviour, there are few general principles concerning them which can be determined and to which any degree of adherence may be

B

expected. Each group of people is distinct and unique in its way of life, its habits and its behaviour, and all of these may exercise an influence on malaria and on plans for its eradication. Variety is the keynote of human conditions in Africa and this must be taken into account fully in the work of malaria eradication, and indeed in that concerned with any other disease in the continent.

BIBLIOGRAPHY

For general background reading, including a chapter on malaria: A. H. Gale, *Epidemic Diseases*, 1959. The literature on malaria, in books and in papers, is immense, and most of it is highly technical. The standard work on the subject is M. F. Boyd (*ed.*), *Malariology*, 1949, 2 vol.; two books written by and for malariologists are G. Macdonald, *The Epidemiology and Control of Malaria*, 1957 and E. Pampana, *A Textbook on Malaria Eradication*, 1963. More general works written by an expert malariologist are, P. F. Russell, *Malaria: basic principles briefly stated*, 1952, and *Man's Mastery of Malaria*, 1955. For the role and work of the World Health Organization: *The First Ten Years of the World Health Organization*, Geneva 1958, and C. Fraser Brockington, *World Health*, 1958.

3 Migrants

WHILE the overall concern of this book is with the influence of people, their behaviour and their ways of life, indeed with all human factors, on malaria and its eradication, population mobility is considered as the feature of particular importance and greatest significance. From the illustration given from north-western Nigeria it is obvious that population movements – why, how and where people move – can affect fundamentally the distribution and incidence of malaria and the measures that are being planned and put into operation for dealing with it. Population movements, both great and small, over long and short distances, have been a feature of Africa in the past and are one of its most important demographic features at the present day. There is no phase of African history which can be understood without reference to the movements of people both before and during it. There are few contemporary problems in the fields of administration and of economic and social development in Africa which are not influenced by population mobility.

Mobility in the past

Population movements in the past often involved large homogeneous groups of people. There are, for example, many tribes in West Africa who trace their origins in lands away to the north of the Sahara desert. Fulani-speaking nomadic pastoralists migrated originally in a south-westerly direction across the Sahara desert to the Fouta Toro in the middle section of the Senegal valley. From here about the twelfth century, they commenced a movement eastward which eventually resulted in their present scattered distribution throughout the northern parts of West Africa (Figure 7). Peoples who now speak languages of the great Bantu linguistic group, dispersed over many centuries throughout Central and much of East Africa and into the southern parts of the continent. The factors influencing and determining movements such as those of the Fulani- and Bantu-speaking peoples are known only in generalized fashion. Certainly the Fulani were influenced by the need of pasture and water for their cattle, and by a search for environments free of the tsetse fly so that their animals would not be stricken with trypanosomiasis. They were also affected, and continue to be influenced, by their contacts with sedentary cultivators in the lands through which they move.

25

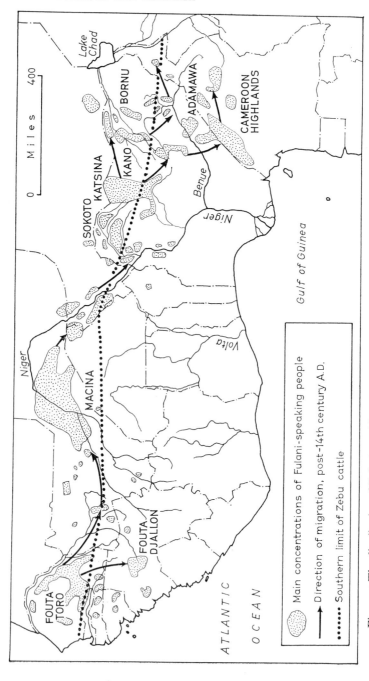

Figure 7 The distribution of Fulani-speaking people in West Africa. (Based on a map by the author in R. W. Steel and R. M. Prothero (ed.) *Geographers and the Tropics*, 1964.)

Intertribal warfare and associated slave raiding and trading were certainly both the cause and effect of population movements. Stronger tribes preyed on weaker neighbours and moved into their lands. Sometimes in this way successive waves of movement were set in motion, which finally extended far away from their point of origin. Disruption of life, caused by devastation and the loss of food supplies through raiding, would result in famines and malnutrition with consequent loss of life by starvation and disease. The remnants of a group who were so affected might move away to a new area leaving their homelands depopulated. There is little doubt of the high degree of population mobility and of great instability in the past in Africa. Evidence is to be found in the myths and legends of tribes at the present day and in the firsthand information which was collected by European explorers and missionaries in the nineteenth century and later by the first colonial administrators.

The aims, and eventual effects, of the administrations established by the European colonial powers were to put an end to the fluid situation that had existed, and to bring about a degree of relative stability. Tribal warfare and slaving ceased and tribes, like the powerful Zande in central Africa who had been in the process of expansion at the expense of weaker neighbours, found that this was no longer possible. They and other tribes found not only that they had to change their habits but that their lands were divided by the new boundaries delimited by the European powers when they parcelled out Africa among themselves. In the case of the Zande, the tribe was divided into three by the boundaries drawn between the Anglo-Egyptian Sudan, Uganda and the Congo Free State. Such divisions as this have led to population movements in recent times; during the era of colonial rule international and internal administrative boundaries, which so frequently divided ethnic groups, were largely ignored and were being continually crossed by people who were of the same group on one side as on the other.

The legacies of mobility in the past may be seen at the present day, for example, in some of the less densely-peopled parts of central Tanganyika. Depopulation of these areas was followed by the growth of vegetation which provided environments favourable for the breeding of the tsetse fly. As a result they frequently became unsuitable for human settlement because of the spread of sleeping sickness. In other parts of Africa, the high incidence of diseases has been responsible for people leaving certain areas and moving elsewhere. Sleeping sickness and river blindness together caused the depopulation of considerable areas in northern Ghana during the early decades of the present century.

In all respects the studies of past population movements – their causes, their manifestations and their implications for the present day – are complex but fascinating.

Pastoral movements

Though colonial rule put an end to much mobility and instability some movements of the past have continued on into the present. These were movements that were considered not to be particularly undesirable in either their cause or their effect. They have thus remained with characteristics which are either unchanged from the past, or which are modified only in part. Those movements which are associated with nomadic pastoral ways of life are the most important; they have continued through several millennia and in some parts of the continent considerable numbers of people are still involved in them at the present day. They represent unbroken continuity from the time of the first domestication of animals, and the original distinction between nomadic pastoralists and sedentary cultivators such as is still rigidly maintained in parts of Africa today. There are a number of types of pastoral movements which differ markedly from one another and represent responses to various conditions and influences. These different types vary in their effects upon malaria and its eradication.

Nomadic pastoralism

Over much of the arid and semi-arid surfaces of the great plains and plateaux of the Old World, especially in North Africa and Asia, pastoral nomads wander with their flocks and herds in search of pasture and water (Figure 8). The availability of these two basic essentials for life is determined by seasonal changes in climates and in these variability and unreliability are dominant features. Sporadic rainfall will produce ephemeral grass growth in limited areas and this is soon exhausted. Supplies of water are rarely more than barely sufficient, often there are severe shortages, and stock and even people may die. On the rare occasions when there is more than bare sufficiency due to abnormal rainfall, this may also produce flooding and consequent devastation. The run-off from rainfall which may collect in shallow depressions is soon used up, both by consumption and by loss through intense evaporation. Shallow wells which are dug to tap sub-surface water are soon overdrawn and then have to be left for supplies to be replenished. Conditions of life in these circumstances are always very difficult and often extremely so. People have no option but to be continually on the move.

The nomadic way of life demands a minimum of material possessions, which can be easily packed and transported from one camping site to another. Dwellings must be easily dismantled and erected. The common forms are tents woven of camel or goat hair or of wool, and simple shelters constructed of a framework of poles covered with skins, mats or leaves. Throughout North Africa and in the Saharan, Libyan and Egyptian deserts tents are the usual dwellings; south of the deserts

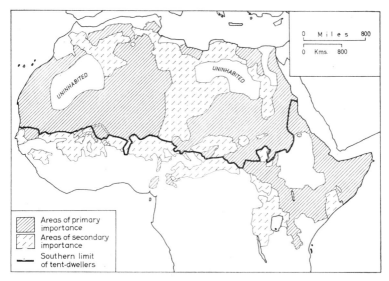

Figure 8 The distribution of pastoralists in North Africa. (Based on a map by the author in Steel and Prothero, *op. cit.*)

shelters predominate (Figure 8). Either of these types is usually found in small groups, forming impermanent settlements whose sites are changing continually.

The movements of truly nomadic groups are difficult to define. Though it may be possible to outline an annual cycle and area of movement in general terms, it is usually impossible to indicate with any precision the routes that will be followed. These are determined by when and where the rain falls and the pasture and water that become available. They change from season to season and from one year to another. The absence of any form of fixed settlement distinguishes true nomads from semi-nomads. The latter return for some period in each year to a focal point (which may not necessarily have permanent dwellings) to cultivate small amounts of crops. True nomads are exclusively pastoral, satisfying all their needs from their animals and regarding with disdain and as inferior, those who cultivate. The way of life which they follow, harsh and at times cruel, has bred in them a sense of independence, a strong conservative spirit, with feelings of superiority and frequently with suspicion of those who live differently.

From the point of view of a central administration and the rule of law nomadic peoples have always been difficult to deal with, as the French found in their long and unrelenting struggle waged with the nomadic tribes of the Sahara in the first half of this century. Independence, conservatism and suspicion are all characteristics which make nomads resentful of control and direction. Nowadays nomadic groups almost everywhere have acquiesced in, or have been forced to accept, the rule of law, and their depredations on caravans and on sedentary oasis dwellers are things of the past. Yet they still rank among people least touched by political, social and economic progress in mid-twentieth-century Africa. In some instances where they have been drawn inevitably into contact with elements of modern life, particularly in areas of oil exploration and exploitation in North Africa, they have shown surprising capacity for adjusting to new ways. But their common tendency is to resist what is new and to cling to what is traditional. In those countries which are newly independent and are attempting to forge ahead with economic and social development, nomads are regarded as an outmoded anachronism; they are out of place in the general desire to achieve modern ways of living. In some of them there are deliberate official policies directed towards nomads to settle them permanently. These policies are meeting with varying degrees of success, dependent to a large extent on the amount of coercion used to obtain the desired end; the most extensive settlements of nomads have taken place in the Asiatic parts of the U.S.S.R. But there are many countries where the successful settlement of nomads has not yet been achieved and many where it has not yet been attempted.

If there are malarious areas in these countries then the nomadic populations may well prove a major factor in the malaria situation and a major problem in its eradication. The fact that nomadic groups are highly mobile means that they are liable to transmit malaria, either as infected carriers or by unwittingly transporting infected mosquitoes, or both. The extent to which this may happen will depend on the timing of movements in relation to the periods of the year when conditions are favourable for malaria transmission (i.e. when mosquito breeding takes place). Particular examples will be examined later of the part played by nomadic movements in malaria in north-west and north-east Africa and in Nigeria, but generally they are a major hazard in eradication programmes and a major deterrent to success.

Basic knowledge of any nomadic population is difficult to obtain, even in simple terms of its size, both because of its mobile character and the unwillingness of its members to divulge information. Censuses of nomads are notorious for their inaccuracy. The absence of defined routes of movement, and the fact that they vary continually, create major problems in planning anti-malarial measures, whether these are by spraying with residual insecticides or through the distribution and administration of drugs. These problems may be eased somewhat in the case of semi-nomads when they spend part of each year at a permanent centre which can be definitely located, though their presence there may not be at the time of the year when anti-malarial measures need to be applied.

Movements are not the only aspect of nomadic life which are a problem. Nomadic dwellings, either tents or shelters, present their own particular difficulties. Their surfaces usually do not satisfactorily retain the toxic effects of insecticide, many of the materials are highly absorptive, and in the case of all the frequent dismantling and re-erection of dwellings inevitably destroys insecticide effectiveness. Insecticide is rubbed off or shaken out in the continual moves that are taking place, and with the Somali nomads of north-east Africa it has been noted that the *inside* surface of the dwelling when it is sprayed may well be the *outside* surface when it is erected again after the encampment has been moved. In an attempt to counter such difficulties, experiments have been made in dipping the coverings of dwellings in insecticide solutions to ensure that they are thoroughly treated. Obviously this can apply only to woven materials.

When complete coverage of the population, in either spraying and drug distribution, is essential for success, nomadic, and even semi-nomadic populations present major difficulties to those in charge of the operations. More specific examples of these difficulties and the possible measures for dealing with them are discussed later.

Transhumance

Certainly for malaria eradication it is necessary to distinguish between the movements of pastoralists who are nomadic and those who practise transhumance. Their movements differ from one another in nature and in their implication. Nomadic movements are represented by a cycle which is usually completed in the course of twelve months and during this time the groups involved are moving frequently. Transhumance involves movements at particular times of year from one grazing area to another by relatively well-defined direct routes. These movements take comparatively little time to complete and the greater part of the year is spent in grazing areas which can be delimited with reasonable precision. Both pasture grounds and the routes between them are thus fixed and permanent as compared with those of nomads. They can be located and delimited with the knowledge that they will be used from one year to the next. Although transhumance is far from being a simple form of human response to environmental circumstances the mobility associated with it is uncomplicated compared with that of nomadism.

The availability of pasture at different times of the year is the major factor in the development of transhumance. Since it is most frequently practised in and adjacent to mountainous areas, the movements associated with it are in a vertical rather than in a horizontal direction – from lower-lying to higher areas and vice versa. Forms of double-transhumance may be practised, with movements to high altitudes in the mountains during the dry conditions of summer, and then to low altitudes on the plains in winter, to avoid low temperatures, and possibly snowfall. Transhumant groups have fixed settlements with permanent dwellings with cultivated lands adjacent to them and these settlements are occupied throughout the year by some members of the group. To them other members who move with the flocks and herds return on one or more occasions during the year. Settlements are usually sited on the floors or lower slopes of valleys and from them ascents are made to higher altitudes in summer and descents to the plains in winter. They are foci of life and pivots of movement, fixed points where all members of the group may be found for some parts of the year. At least at these times transhumant pastoralists may be located for applying malaria eradication measures; there are no problems in locating the permanent settlements for spraying, though they may be difficult of access because of the nature of the terrain.

Locating and contacting pastoralists when they are actually involved in transhumance are more difficult but still much easier than when dealing with nomads. Movements either to high pastures in summer or to low pastures in winter are in most instances dictated by the nature of the terrain and are along well-defined routes which are followed each year. The timing of these movements is also reasonably well-defined, so that it is possible to know with some certainty where people are at any particular time in the year. Tents are the usual form of dwelling during journeys to and from and at the grazing grounds. They may present similar problems for spraying as do the tents of nomads, but at least they can be located more easily for treatment and they are made of woven materials.

Pastoral ways of life, though they present many elements that are strongly traditional, are nonetheless changing. Some of these changes and their possible effects on malaria eradication will be discussed in later chapters. Except where changes are being forced upon pastoralists, or where they are being brought so immediately into contact with new ways that they have no option but to accept them, the evolution to new forms of living is slow. It extends over many years and is often barely perceptible. Changes that are being effected at such slow rates are unlikely greatly to affect programmes of malaria eradication, and they must therefore be planned to accept and deal with the various types of mobility associated with pastoral ways of life.

Pilgrimage

Although their antiquity may not be comparable with pastoral move-ments, pilgrim movements of various kinds within and between many countries, are often of considerable age. They are an important element in the continuity of mobility from the past to the present in Africa. Some pilgrimages are made over distances of only a few miles to local shrines, others involve journeys of transcontinental proportions. The greatest attractions for pilgrims from all over the world are the holy places of Islam at Mecca and Medina. In fulfilling the requirements of their religion, that they should make the *haj* at least once during their lifetime, many hundreds of thousands of faithful Muslim pilgrims converge each year upon Saudi Arabia from all parts of the world (Figure 9). The greatest numbers of pilgrims come from the Middle East, where their religion originated, and from North Africa to which it was quickly taken by the Arab invasions in the seventh and eighth centuries A.D. Islam penetrated across the Sahara desert to West Africa some three or four centuries later and to East Africa down the Nile valley and by way of the Red Sea and the Indian Ocean. Being of a strong proselytizing nature, with every devout Moslem a potential missionary committed to converting the unbelievers, and by its appeal to people not only as a religion but as a way of life that is laid down for them to follow, Islam continues to spread rapidly among the peoples of Africa, much more rapidly than Christianity, the other great religion with which it competes for converts in the continent. Increasing numbers of converts mean increasing numbers of pilgrims. While Muslims from West Africa have moved for many centuries along the

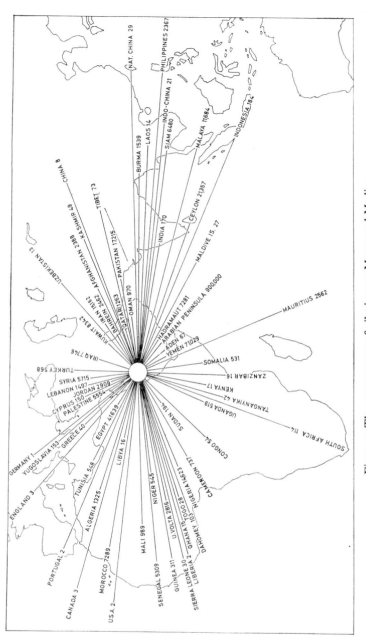

Figure 9 The convergence of pilgrims on Mecca and Medina. (Based on a map prepared by the World Health Organization.)

routes that take them by way of Lake Chad, eastwards to the Nile valley and thence to the Red Sea coast, they are moving now in greater numbers than ever before. These increases reflect also improvements in means of transport and greater security along the routes travelled.

The implications for all aspects of public health of this great annual convergence of pilgrims on Mecca and Medina are tremendous. Great improvements in facilities for checking upon the health of pilgrims have been introduced in recent times, but still there are considerable risks of the spread of infectious diseases. Pilgrims returning from the *haj* may take with them the infections which they have acquired to the countries through which they pass and may bring them to their own countries. The particular implications of pilgrim movements for malaria and its eradication will be discussed in the chapter on the Republic of the Sudan, the country in Africa which is most especially affected by this type of mobility. It is on the Sudan that the majority of African pilgrims converge before they cross to Jidda, the port of entry for pilgrims on the eastern shore of the Red Sea. It is back to Suakin in the Sudan that they come before commencing their return journeys throughout Africa.

Local population movements

While pastoralism and pilgrimage involve movements of people over great distances, there are also movements that take place over only a few miles but which are still significant in their effects on malaria and schemes for eradication. These are seasonal movements of farmers and fishermen.

Among some agricultural communities in Africa lands are cultivated for distances of up to ten miles from the permanent settlements. Daily work on the farms is necessary during periods of maximum activity in the agricultural calendar—when the land is being prepared for cultivation, when continual weeding of growing crops is necessary, and at harvest time. In economic terms the losses through time and energy wasted in journeys to and from farms are considerable, and to reduce them temporary shelters are often erected on farms. In these shelters the farmers and their labourers may live for days and even weeks on end, with only occasional visits to their permanent homes. This practice affects malaria and measures for its eradication in two ways. In the first place it causes a dispersal of a section of the population. Contact with these people is made much more difficult when they are scattered in small groups over a wide area, on patches of cultivated land that may be separated from one another by a dense vegetation cover which in places may be virtually impenetrable. Locating people for the purposes of drug distribution, when they are distributed in this way, is a difficult task and it is well-nigh impossible to obtain complete coverage of them all. Movement may be possible only along bush paths along which it is easy to lose one's way without local knowledge or local co-operation. In attempting to find people under these circumstances the wear and tear on personnel and equipment is excessive.

Besides the problems of a dispersed population there are also those which are caused by the temporary shelters in which the farm workers live. Unless these are included in the cycle of insecticide spraying, they are likely to become foci of malaria transmission since they provide acceptable indoor resting places for vectors. The inevitable and obvious difficulties of locating these shelters are as great as the difficulties of locating the people who occupy them. Often they are erected after the spraying of the area in which they occur has taken place. The situation is further aggravated by the fact that they are occupied at times of the year when malaria transmission is most intense. During the early weeks of the wet season agricultural activity is at its maximum and the temporary shelters on farms are occupied: with the increased amounts of water in which breeding can take place this is also the period when there is likely to be an explosive increase in the number of mosquitoes.

During the times of the year when water is low in the great rivers of Africa – Niger and Benue, Nile and Congo – the sandbanks exposed in their beds become the sites of temporary settlements, established by fishermen and their families who live in rough shelters. These structures are often even more inaccessible than those on farmlands and for similar reasons are likely to be missed in the cycles of insecticide spraying. The fact that they are sited near water means almost certainly that they will be used as resting places by mosquitoes in large numbers. They are thus ideal foci for malaria transmission.

Besides the problems created by these temporary shelters and the migrant fishermen who inhabit them, there are also malaria problems associated with the large numbers of people who live permanently on the rivers of Africa. They gain their livelihood either from fishing or from trading, and frequently by combining these activities. They live generally in large canoes, with a section of each covered with woven mats or some other material to provide living quarters. Those who trade may travel distances of many hundreds of miles, often along stretches of waterway which cannot be navigated by more sophisticated craft. They are a migrant element which is particularly difficult to contact in malaria work, or for any other purpose, for several obvious reasons. The shelters are likely to go unsprayed and the people without drugs, and yet from the very nature of that life they are likely to be continually in contact with large numbers of malaria vectors.

Changes in settlement patterns

While it seems unlikely that there will be substantial changes in the foreseeable future in the lives of people who live on or adjacent to rivers

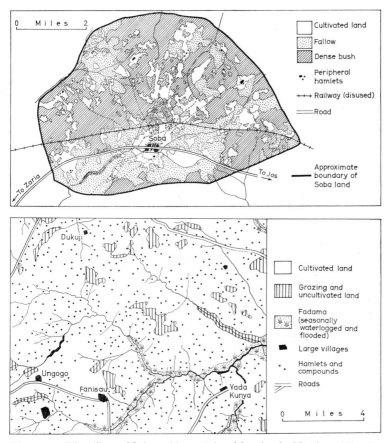

Figure 10a The village of Soba and its peripheral hamlets in Northern Nigeria. b The settlement pattern in a densely populated part of Kano Province, Northern Nigeria.

in Africa, there have been changes taking place in patterns of agricultural settlement which are both favourable and unfavourable to malaria eradication. The development of peaceful conditions under colonial administration brought greater security in the countryside, and farmlands, some way distant from main fortified settlements which provided protection in former troubled times, have now become the sites for permanent hamlets. The hamlets have developed as off-shoots from the main settlements, as at Soba a large village in Zaria Province in Northern Nigeria (Figure 10a). Soba was formerly a fortified settlement of some importance and the remnants of its protecting wall and ditch are still visible. Around Soba and up to a maximum distance of about four miles peripheral hamlets have been established in recent years, by people from the main village who in the past would have gone out to their farms in these areas only for temporary visits.

The founding of these new small settlements is also part of a process in the evolution settlement and land use, in which the areas of un-inhabited no-man's-land which existed between towns and large villages in former troubled times have been taken into cultivation. This process is related not only to the peace and security established in the present century, but also to increases in population and to the consequent need for increased amounts of farmland. In most parts of Africa which support high rural population densities (over *c.* 500 persons per square mile) – for example, in Kano Province in Northern Nigeria and in parts of Rwanda and Burundi in East Africa – the settlement pattern has developed as one of occasional large villages and towns which function as local centres, with a dense scatter of homesteads, individually or in small groups over the farmland which lies between (Figure 10b). This pattern permits the fullest use to be made of the maximum amounts of available cultivable land, and thus for high densities to be supported.

From the point of view of agricultural production these developments are most desirable; for malaria eradication, for the application of other public health measures (e.g. the provision of dispensaries), and for any schemes for improvements in social services (e.g. schools), they present many problems. For malaria eradication the dispersed population increases the difficulties of making contact and of ensuring complete coverage in either insecticide spraying or in drug distribution. Much more time is needed for the greater distances that have to be covered than would be necessary if all the population lived in compact nucleated settlements. Consequently there is a rise in the cost of operations.

Recent population mobility

Some types of population mobility came to an end with the establishment of peace and security in Africa under European colonial administrations; the upheavals and removals of people consequent on tribal warfare and slaving no longer took place. But these more stable conditions in turn influenced the development of new types of population movement.

Downhill movements

In many parts of Africa from early in the present century movements of people began to take place from mountainous areas. Here in the past difficult terrain had provided weaker groups with refuge and relative safety from the depredations of stronger neighbours. In West Africa, for example, these movements are still in progress from the Fouta Djallon plateau in Guinea, from the hills in the north of Togo and in Dahomey, from the Jos Plateau in Nigeria and from the Adamawa and Cameroon highlands farther east. One possibility with these downhill movements is that people, who formerly lived either in malaria-free environments or in ones where the transmission season was short and not intense, because of the effect of altitude on vector breeding, will come to settle in more highly malarious areas at lower altitudes and will succumb heavily to the disease because they lack acquired tolerance.

Frequently these movements are accompanied by changes in farming practices. In remote mountain fastnesses conservative methods of farming are necessary, because of the limited amounts of cultivable land that are available. One of the characteristic features of highland landscapes are the many miles of laboriously constructed and well-cared-for terraces, which permit the maximum use of cultivable land on steep slopes and at the same time reduce the dangers of soil erosion. With migration down to lowland areas in recent decades conservative methods of farming have been abandoned. Clearance and cultivation have taken place indiscriminately on the much greater areas of land available, with little thought for the preservation of either soil cover or soil fertility. Energetic farmers have wrought destruction over large areas in this way, and in some instances resettlement schemes have been established in an attempt to control their activities and to eliminate wasteful methods. These schemes have been interesting experiments, not only in controlled farming but also in new methods of administration and the organization of social welfare (e.g. the provision of schools, dispensaries and other amenities). Many have been established with very limited capital investment and with strong emphasis in their development on principles of self-help and community work. There are several advantages in applying measures for malaria eradication to resettled populations. Numbers of people, their exact location, the nature of their settlements and methods of administration are known, and, even more important, the people are accustomed to some amount of discipline and control. The nature of malaria eradication and the reasons for certain measures can be more easily explained to them, and they are likely to be more amenable and cooperative in their relations with eradication teams.

Trading movements

Even in the unsettled conditions of the past in Africa there were always people who were prepared to face difficulties and dangers in return for economic gain. The great caravan trade across the Sahara, linking West and North Africa, was of great antiquity and it began to decline seriously only when European penetration inland from the coast of West Africa made trade by sea a better proposition. The security established early in the present century made possible a great expansion of trade without fear of attack and depredation. This increase in the exchange of commodities, both locally and over longer distances, was inevitably accompanied by increased movements of people. In West Africa, Hausa traders from Northern Nigeria and Yoruba market women are to be found trading in the markets far beyond the boundaries of their home countries. Dioula merchants from Mali travel as far afield as Leopoldville, having extended the range of their traditional trade with modern means of transport.

In the more restricted but nonetheless interesting field of local trade and internal exchange, markets are held in different centres, usually on a defined cyclic pattern and traders travel regularly from one to another. Each market serves a hinterland of varying extent, depending on its importance, its distance from adjacent markets and the means of communication. People come to them over long and short distances and they serve not only economic but also social functions. They are the meeting places for relatives and friends, for the exchange of news and gossip as well as of goods. But in bringing about these increased movements and contacts between people the influence of trade and of markets may not be entirely favourable. In the dust-laden air that rises from a Moroccan *souk*, or where people jostle closely together in a Mossi market in the Haute Volta, for example, there are infinite possibilities for the transmission of diseases.

Labour migration

During the relatively brief era of colonial rule in Africa, the greatest changes in the character of population mobility were initiated and developed, both directly and indirectly, through European influence and organization. By the exploitation of agricultural and mineral resources during the last sixty years Africa has been brought into the mainstream of world economy. The production of traditional crops in indigenous rural economies has been increased to satisfy export demands, and new crops have been introduced. Senegal and Northern Nigeria produce the greater part of the groundnuts which enter into world trade, and cotton from the Sudan and Uganda helps to supply the textile industries of Britain and Europe. Cocoa, which was introduced into West Africa only at the end of the nineteenth century, is grown by hundreds of thousands of farmers in Ghana and Western Nigeria, who now produce more than two-thirds of the world tonnage of the crop. Attracted by African land and labour, Europeans acquired land for large-scale agricultural production on farms and plantations in all except the western parts of the continent – vine and citrus in North Africa; coffee, sisal and tea in Kenya and Tanganyika and oil palm in the Congo; tobacco in Southern Rhodesia and cereals in South Africa; these are among the more important crops that they have cultivated.

In addition to agricultural development there has also been a widespread and, in some instances, large-scale exploitation of minerals – phosphates and oil in North Africa; iron ore, manganese, bauxite and tin in West Africa; copper in Katanga and Northern Rhodesia and gold and diamonds in South Africa. Industries have been developed, sometimes in association with mineral exploitation. All these profound economic changes have produced conditions which are very different from those in the past, and in varying degrees they have all influenced the development of labour migration as a new form of population mobility. They have attracted migrants in a way comparable to that of the coalfields and industrial centres which drew people from the rural areas of Britain in the nineteenth century.

A conservative estimate suggests that at least five million people are involved each year in migrant labour movements in Africa south of the Sahara. Those who migrate are influenced primarily by a desire to enjoy the relatively higher standards of living which can be obtained by contributing their labour to, and by acquiring skills in, developing economic enterprises. There are demands for migrant labour in areas of export cash-crop production, on large farms and plantations, in mines and factories and at commercial centres and seaports. Not only do these attract people, the migrants themselves are also influenced by conditions in their home areas. In the major source areas of migrants there is often pressure of population on resources, with serious shortages of land for cultivation and resultant low standards of living. Circumstances may be so severe that people are left with little alternative but to migrate in order to supplement their incomes. A variety of other factors – social, psychological and political – may influence the development of

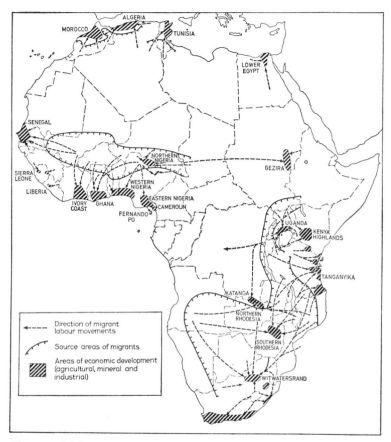

Figure 11 Main movements of migrant labour in Africa. (Based on maps by the author in *Bulletin, World Health Organization, Geographical Journal*, and Steel and Prothero, *op. cit.*)

migrant labour. A recent investigation among one group of people in West Cameroon revealed that fear of witchcraft was a potent factor in causing them to leave home and to seek work on nearby plantations. But overall, investigations in Africa have shown that the influence of economic factors is dominant in the development of labour migration.

While there is a considerable amount of information on the motives for labour migration and on its effects, there is comparatively little known of the patterns of movements and of the routes which migrants follow in their journeys to and from work. For those concerned with the role of migrant labourers in the spread of diseases this kind of information is of vital importance; but at the present time it is not possible to give more than generalized indication of the patterns of movements for the whole of Africa. Three groups of movements may be distinguished – those of North Africa, of West Africa, and of East, Central and South Africa – and they differ from one another not only in their geographical location but also in some of their characteristic features (Figure 11).

West Africa

The most straightforward pattern of movements is that in West Africa where migrations in general follow a north–south axis. Migrants originate particularly from Mali, Haute Volta and Niger, and from the northern parts of Ghana and Nigeria. They find employment in the more economically advanced regions to the west and south – in the areas of groundnut cultivation in Senegal and Northern Nigeria, in the cocoa-growing regions of Ivory Coast, Ghana and Western Nigeria, in the iron ore mines of Sierra Leone and Liberia and at the ports and major towns like Dakar, Abidjan, Kumasi, Accra, Ibadan and Lagos.

To reach these places of work migrants have to travel long distances, 600 miles and more on their way to work and then the same again on their return journeys. Journeys were formerly made on foot and, even though the growth of communications has had an important influence on movements, some journeys are still in part made in this way. There is no detailed information on how the different means of transport are used, or of the time that is taken on various journeys. Both of these are very relevant factors in the timing of migrations which generally are annual events in West Africa. Migrants leave home to seek work between late September and November, at the beginning of the dry season after the harvest has been taken; they return home again in the following April and May to cultivate their farms with the onset of the rains. The distinct seasonal variations in climate between one part of the year and another thus permit migrations to be integrated into the annual cycle of activity. The fact that the movements are seasonal in character is relevant to their influence on malaria and its eradication. These influences vary in their nature and in their effects with the seasons of malaria transmission in the areas from which the migrants originate, those in which they work, and those through which they pass on their journeys.

East, Central and South Africa

In contrast to West Africa the movements on the eastern side of the continent generally involve migrants in longer absences from home, usually for one or two years. There are some movements which are seasonal in character, like the migration of labour from the East African mainland to the islands of Zanzibar and Pemba for the clove harvest. The pattern of movements is more complicated, but here also migrants originate from poor and often over-populated areas like Rwanda and Burundi, the West Nile District of Uganda and the Southern Highlands Province of Tanganyika, and seek work in regions of comparatively advanced economic development. Cotton-growing areas in Buganda, European farms in the Kenya Highlands, sisal estates in Tanganyika, the Katanga and Northern Rhodesian Copperbelt, and gold mines of the Witwatersrand in South Africa have been the major foci of attraction. Large towns like Kampala, Nairobi, Mombasa, Salisbury and Johannesburg are magnets to people from impoverished rural areas who see in them the prospects of a good living. The fact that these hopes are fulfilled for only a minority has in no way stemmed the flow.

Characteristics of labour migration

Much of the migrant labour in West Africa is employed on enterprises which are individually on a small scale, though are collectively of great economic importance. Each cocoa farmer in Ghana or in Western Nigeria produces from only a few acres of land though the production from the two countries is a high proportion of the total world production of cocoa. The movements of migrants to work in these enterprises are spontaneous, with no formal organization at any stage. The only organized recruiting of labour in West Africa takes place in Eastern Nigeria for work on the plantations of the island of Fernando Po, and this is controlled by an international agreement between Nigeria and Spain. Formerly labour was recruited in Haute Volta for work in the Ivory Coast. Though there is generally no organized recruitment of labour there are various informal but effective ways in which migrants are helped to find work. The towns of Bouaké in the north of Ivory Coast and Kumasi in the Ashanti region of Ghana are both well known as centres where migrants can obtain information on the labour requirements of any part of these two countries at any particular time. This information is picked up in the markets, at the railway stations or at the lorry parks.

Consequent on this spontaneity and lack of organization there has been a dearth of information on West African labour migration compared with that for other parts of the continent. Large-scale enterprises which recruit labour under contract in East, Central and South Africa can provide details of where labourers come from, of the routes by which they travel to and from work, and of the lengths of time which they spend away from home. The largest recruiting organization in Africa is the Witwatersrand Native Labour Association (WENELA) which recruits for the mining industries in the Republic of South Africa. It arranges for the engagement of migrant labourers and for their transport to and from work; in the past, for example, workers from southern Tanganyika were flown down to Bechuanaland and then completed the journey to the Witwatersrand by road. Formerly it recruited as far north as Tanganyika and Nyasaland, north-west to the border between Northern Rhodesia and Angola and eastward in Moçambique. The range of its recruiting activities has been curtailed in recent years with the assumption of power by independent African governments and their determination to fight South African apartheid policies in every way possible. Thus recruiting for the South African mines has been stopped in Tanganyika, at some considerable loss to those who went as labourers and also to the country which benefited from the cash with which they returned when their contracts were at an end.

Recruiting organizations, of course, are not the only source of information on labour migration; both individual and collective studies have been made in various parts of the continent of different aspects of this phenomenon. Its immense economic and social significance has long been recognized and increasingly in recent times it has been shown to be of importance in the field of public health. Preoccupation with its economic and social aspects has resulted in studies concentrating upon the motives and consequences of migrant labour. There is, for example, much more known of the influence of labour migration on divorce rates and prostitution than about the numbers who migrate and the routes which they travel. While the former are of prime importance in their influence upon social stability, and indeed have some influence upon public health, the absence of any detailed information on the latter is a serious lack in planning malaria eradication programmes. Even the somewhat better information for the eastern and southern parts of the continent does not provide anything like the amount of detail that is required on the volume, timing and pattern of labour migration.

Population mobility, in all the various forms that have been outlined, may menace public health, both by assisting in the maintenance and the spread of diseases and by obstructing measures for their eradication. In the following chapters various aspects of population mobility are examined in different countries and regions of Africa, and some of the relationships of these movements to malaria and its eradication are discussed and illustrated. The more precise functions of population movements as factors in the epidemiology of malaria have still to be investigated and evaluated in most parts of Africa.

BIBLIOGRAPHY

There is a very extensive literature on pastoral nomadism for North Africa, particularly in French. Authoritative papers on this subject for North Africa and South-west Asia are collected under the title 'Nomads and Nomadism in the Arid Zone', in the *International Social Science Journal*, **11**, 1959, 481, published by UNESCO. Population movements in Africa are reviewed by the author in the following papers: 'Population Movements and Problems of Malaria Eradication in Africa', *Bulletin of the World Health Organization*, **24**, 1961, 405; 'Continuity and Change in African Population Mobility', in R. W. Steel and R. M. Prothero (*ed.*), *Geographers and the Tropics: Liverpool Essays*, 1964; 'Migrant Labour in West Africa', *Journal of Local Administration Overseas*, **1**, 1962, 149. See also: Commission for Technical Cooperation in Africa south of the Sahara, *Migrant Labour in Africa South of the Sahara*, 1961, and Hans E. Panofsky, 'Migratory Labour in Africa – a bibliographical note', *Journal of Modern African Studies*, **1**, 1963, 521.

4 The Republic of the Sudan

THE particular significance of the Sudan, for malaria eradication throughout the whole of Africa, lies in the fact that it is the first country in the continent to embark on a programme which is planned to end with country-wide eradication of the disease. Pre-eradication surveys were begun in 1961 and were to develop in 1963 into the attack phase which would mark the beginning of the real attempt at eradication. This programme is altogether an ambitious one, for what is contemplated would be a major undertaking for any country in Africa at the present time. In the Sudan, with a total population of twelve million of whom almost all are estimated to be at risk to malaria, the situation that exists and the problems to be faced in eradication are of mammoth proportions. Many of these problems are directly related to and influenced by the geography of the country and its inhabitants.

Geographical diversity

With an area of nearly a million square miles the Republic of the Sudan is the largest country in Africa. It extends from the Red Sea coast in the east to the eastern borders of the Sahara desert in the west. Its greater extent is from north to south; from the 22° N parallel of latitude, which forms the frontier with Egypt, Sudanese territory extends southward to approximately latitude 4° N where its boundary is with the Congo (Leopoldville), Uganda and Kenya. To the east its boundary runs with Ethiopia and with Ubangi-Shari, Chad and Libya to the west. Such great extent in latitude gives rise to an enormous range in environmental conditions – from the virtually rainless, and certainly waterless, deserts in the north of the country to the high rainfall of the equatorial forests in the south. Plains, mountains and swamps all occur on a major scale within the Sudan's boundaries, but the single greatest physical feature is the system of the Nile rivers and their tributaries. This dominates almost the whole of the country. From the extreme south the White Nile comes from its source in Lake Victoria in Uganda and flowing northward receives the waters of the Albert Nile, the Bahr el Ghazal and the Bahr el Jebel from the west. Then in the great swamp region of the Sudd the Nile spreads out and almost loses its identity as a river, providing only a poor waterway for movement and subject to enormous water losses from evaporation. Downstream of the Sudd region and just south of Malakal, the first major tributary from the west, the Sobat, flows in from its source in the highlands of Ethiopia.

At Khartoum the relatively 'white' silt-free waters of the White Nile are joined by the 'blue' silt-laden waters of the Blue Nile which have their main source in Lake Tana in Ethiopia. The combined waters form the main Nile River which then flows through the northern parts of the Sudan into Egypt and thence to the Mediterranean Sea. Only one major tributary joins north of the Khartoum confluence; the

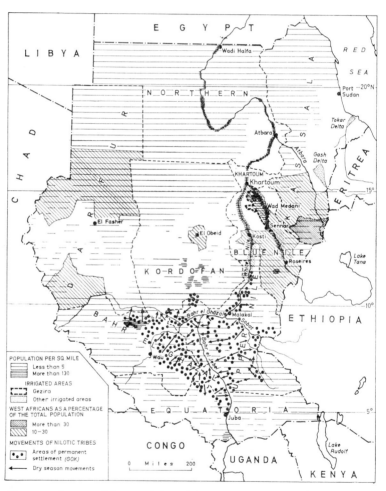

Figure 12 Aspects of the population of the Republic of the Sudan. (Based on a map by the author in *Bulletin, World Health Organization.*)

Atbara from the east, a stream which is without flowing water for many months of each year.

The waters of the two Niles and their tributaries are not as vital to the Sudan as they are to Egypt, at least not in the south of the country where there is sufficient rainfall for crops to be grown without irrigation, and to provide water for human and animal needs. But in the central and, even more, in the northern parts of the country the river waters assume an importance comparable to that which they have in Egypt. The population is distributed with an emphatic concentration of people in lands immediately adjacent to the rivers (Figure 12). Though improvements in water supplies have been effected in areas away from rivers during the last decade and this progress is continuing, there is no likelihood of the valleys of the two Niles being superseded in their traditional attraction for human settlement.

Water from the rivers makes cultivation possible in areas that are otherwise arid wastes for much of each year, except for the brief periods when the aridity is relieved by the small amounts (on average less than eight inches) of rain which fall. Away from the river valleys in the central and northern parts of the Sudan the natural environment for the most part permits only a sparse population of nomadic pastoralists whose herds, mainly of camels, sheep and goats, but with some cattle, are limited in size and are of poor quality because of the general shortages of grazing and of water. Many of these nomads, during the height of the dry season, move with their animals to the lands adjacent to the rivers, seeking water and grazing for their animals and employment for themselves in the agricultural developments that the Nile waters have made possible.

Pilgrim movements

Though it does not provide an uninterrupted line of communication, the Nile has been used as the principal north–south routeway for many centuries in this part of Africa. At right-angles to it is an east–west routeway, probably of comparable antiquity, which follows the relatively open lands, with grass and a light tree cover, in the sahel – savannah vegetation zone between latitudes 10° N and 16° N, which extend right the way across the continent for about 4,000 miles from the Atlantic Ocean to the Red Sea. Along this routeway invaders and traders have passed from times immemorial, and for many centuries it has been used by faithful Muslims making the pilgrimage to the Holy Places of Islam at Mecca and Medina and on their return journeys. The ancestors of tribes that now occupy some of the northern parts of West Africa came this way in the past and pilgrims have traversed it in both directions from about the twelfth century A.D. There is, for example, a detailed record of the magnificent pilgrimage of Mansa Musa,* the Mandingo monarch, which he made in the fourteenth century; but far more significant in numbers and in their implications, have been the journeys of many millions of much poorer though equally devout West African Muslims.

In the past these journeys were made on foot or by animal transport and inevitably took many years to complete – from West Africa eastward to the Nile valley, thence to the Red Sea coast where at Suakin pilgrims embark for the sea journey to Jidda, the port for Mecca. Pilgrims may return to their homes twenty or thirty years after having set out and many, for various reasons, have never returned. At the present time as Islam claims more and more converts in Africa the volume of pilgrimage continues to increase and pilgrims are aided by developments in communications. For the wealthy and more sophisticated pilgrims from West Africa, who wish to complete their journeys in a short time, there are the facilities of air travel. Arranging charter flights from places like Kano and Niamey to Mecca and back, is a feature of the business of West African travel agencies, and each year about 2,000 make the *haj* from Nigeria in this way. But the majority of pilgrims are poor and unable to afford fast air travel and they still make their way along the traditional routes. About 10,000 leave Nigeria officially each year to travel overland. A few may still go on foot for some parts of the way but the majority use various forms of motor transport. Certain features of the pilgrim journeys of the past are retained at the present day and faster movement by bus or lorry over the main stages of the journey is still frequently interspersed with long periods spent at various places *en route*. At these pilgrims may remain for several weeks or even months, to earn sufficient money to continue on their way. Some may therefore still take years to complete their journeys to Mecca and to return home.

Whatever routes or means of transport pilgrims may take from West Africa they converge upon the Republic of Sudan. Those who travel by air pass through either Khartoum or Port Sudan and are subject to the usual strict international health and quarantine regulations. Those who come overland should enter the Sudan by one of four main routes of entry: *via* Biltine and Kaktum to El Fasher; *via* Beid and south to Zalingei to El Obeid; *via* Kafia Kugi, Buram and Nahud to El Obeid; *via* Nyala, Muglad and the Nuba mountains to El Obeid. On entering

* E. W. Bovill, *The Golden Trade of the Moors*, 1958.

the country they should pass through one of the frontier control posts and at these they would be subject to international travel regulations. They should possess valid international certificates showing that they have been vaccinated against smallpox and inoculated against yellow fever; but it has been estimated that only about 25 per cent of those travelling on some of the routes fulfil these requirements. For anyone who wishes for any reason to avoid official control there is no difficulty in doing so. There are more than 1,500 miles of open boundary on the western side of the Sudan which people may cross if they wish by a maze of roads and tracks over which it is impossible to maintain effective control. When the Sudan reaches the consolidation phase in its malaria eradication programme these pilgrim movements across its western boundary will certainly be a possible source for the introduction of fresh malaria infections, and provision will have to be made against this happening.

Population movements within the Sudan

Besides pilgrim movements through the Sudan, there are also various mobile elements in the population within the country which influence the transmission of malaria and other diseases and are likely to affect eradication measures. Some of these are to be found in those parts of the country where economic development is relatively advanced, for on these areas pilgrims and others converge in search of work. A distinct group of people involved are the 'Westerners', a collective name given to those who come from the lands west of the Nile rivers and from as far afield as West Africa. In the census of 1955 they numbered about 1,500,000, representing 20 per cent of the total population of the Sudan.

The 'Westerner' elements are economically most important in the Gezira, between the White and the Blue Niles, where, by the control of water from the rivers, the large-scale cultivation of cotton by irrigation has been made possible. Here, and farther east in the agricultural developments taking place in the Gash and Tokar deltas, the 'Westerners' are noted for the excellence of their labour in contrast to many of the local Sudanese. They are prepared to pioneer the settlement of land with potential for development, but where conditions in the early stages may be difficult and unattractive. In many respects they are essential to the economic well-being of the Sudan, not only in the Gezira – the major area of crop production for export – but also for the part they play in the cultivation of grain and other food crops throughout the central plains from Kordofan to the Ethiopian border.

In the first census of the Sudan in 1955 200,000 West Africans (who are part of the 'Westerner' group) were counted and the actual number was undoubtedly greater, since many registered as Sudanese though their claim to nationality would not be legally upheld. In the southern parts of Kassala Province they comprise more than thirty per cent of the population, and between twenty and thirty per cent in other parts of Kassala and in Blue Nile, Kordofan and Darfur Provinces (Figure 12). Some of them are pilgrims who have never returned home to West Africa, others are political refugees from Northern Nigeria in the early years of the present century. Although it is the children and grandchildren of these people who are now living in the Sudan, they still retain many of the distinctive features of their forbears in language, culture and way of life. It is a fascinating experience for anyone who knows West Africa to travel through some of the villages in the Gezira, especially to the south of Singa, where in appearance they are similar to, and carry the same names as, villages in Northern Nigeria. In the larger towns – Khartoum, Omdurman, Wad Medani, El Fasher and El Obeid – there are large and distinct quarters which are occupied almost exclusively by West Africans. It is to their kinsmen in these villages and in these quarters in the towns that migrant pilgrims come on their way to and from Mecca – to receive food and shelter and to be assisted in finding work if they require it.

Besides the 'Westerners' the other mobile elements in the Sudan are to be found mainly in the ninety-two per cent of the total population which was classed as rural in the census. In the rural population a major distinction was made between sedentary and nomadic groups; the proportions of these groups varied from one province to another, with the highest percentages of nomads in the northern and predominantly Arab parts of the country.

The proportions, seventy-eight per cent sedentary and fourteen per cent nomadic, for the country as a whole are misleading; the latter figure was considered definitely to be an underestimate of the elements of the population which are mobile, for at least part if not the whole of every year. The seasonal movements of some peoples in the three southern provinces of the Sudan, for example, were not considered in determining the nomadic elements in the population. Furthermore, whenever this was possible the census enumeration took place during the cultivation and harvest seasons, which are times of the year when the greatest numbers of people are settled, though some of them only temporarily, and this further favoured the inflation of the sedentary category. Making allowance for these circumstances and depending on the definitions used, the Chief Census Officer estimated that not less than

Table 3 Sedentary and nomadic rural population in the Republic of the Sudan

Province	Population (000s)				
	Total	Rural			
		Sedentary		Nomadic	
	Number	Number	per cent	Number	per cent
Bahr el Ghazal	999	974	98	—	—
Blue Nile	2,070	1,781	86	145	7
Darfur	1,329	1,010	76	265	20
Equatoria	903	881	98	—	—
Kassala	941	290	31	502	53
Khartoum	505	197	39	53	10
Kordofan	1,762	1,293	73	354	20
Northern	873	718	82	67	8
Upper Nile	889	879	99	—	—
Sudan	10,263	8,023	78	1,386	14

Source: K. J. Krotki, *21 facts about the Sudanese, Khartoum* 1958.

fifteen per cent and up to forty per cent of the total population might be classed as nomadic.

In parts of the southern Sudan, south of latitude 12° N, the ways of life of the Nilotic tribes are regulated by the régime of the White Nile and because of variations in the physical environment during the year they are virtually obliged to migrate (Figure 12). The permanent villages of these people are on high ground (*gok*) and are occupied during the period from April/May to November/December; this is the wet season when much of the lower-lying land is flooded. During these months they cultivate crops and their cattle are kept on the pasture that is available near to the villages. In December when the rains have ceased the cattle have to be taken farther afield to find grazing but the distances still make it possible for them to be brought back each evening. As the dry season continues in January and February, pasture and water become scarce on the higher ground and the cattle are then moved to pastures on the edges of the permanent swamps or near the large rivers (*toich*). Apart from the old people and some of the children the whole populations of the villages move with the cattle. The distances they travel may be as great as those covered by true nomads in the north of the Sudan, but in the census these Nilotic tribes were classed as sedentary. When they move to dry season pastures they concentrate in areas where, because of the presence of water, there is likely to be continual mosquito breeding and thus malaria transmission. In the wet season with the widespread rains there is an extension of the areas in which mosquitoes breed to the *gok*, where the population is then concentrated. As a result of their seasonal movements the majority of people are thus likely to be in areas where malaria transmission is possible at any time of the year.

To the west of the White Nile in Kordofan Province there are Arab cattle nomads, whose traditional economy has been modified in recent years since they have begun to grow some cotton, though this occupies them for only a limited period of the year. The annual cycle of movements of the Humr, one of these tribes, takes them through four zones of differing environments – from wet season pastures (*Babanusa*) to land which they cultivate (*Muglad*), thence to dry season pasture (*Bahr*), with a zone of transition (*Qoz*) through which they pass between the first two zones and the third. At the height of the dry season some of the tribe may even move out of Kordofan altogether into Upper Nile Province. For the Humr as a whole the general tendency is for the tribe to be most concentrated in the *Babanusa* and most dispersed in the *Bahr*, but there is no regular pattern. In the course of these movements there is also a considerable amount of fission and fusion among various groups within the tribe, with frequent changes in their composition.

In the dry season pastures particularly, such disparate factors as the availability of grass and water, personal disputes, the siting of the camps of other groups or even the desire to hunt giraffe, may influence the movements of people. Dwellings can be dismantled and packed within an hour and re-erected again in about two hours and a camp may be moved twenty miles in a day. The distribution of the Humr is thus continually changing throughout the year, and from one year to another would never be the same in any of the zones in which they move. A nomadic way of life based on a pastoralism is the only one of which these people can conceive; their system of values is related to it and to their cattle which make it necessary. Although some of the Humr have begun to cultivate cotton this has not fundamentally changed their way of life, and it has in fact become another factor influencing their movements during the course of the year. In each of the different environmental zones through which they move during the year these people are likely to encounter different malaria conditions. Any programme for eradication would therefore need to take into account not only the movements of the Humr but also these differences of environment. Eradication measures would have to be designed that were relevant to each of these zones.

The Blue Nile malaria eradication pilot project

The problems of malaria eradication in the Sudan were originally evaluated in a pilot project that was located in the Blue Nile Province between the White and Blue Niles. Its headquarters was at Sennar and the project area extended thence southward to the boundary with Ethiopia (Figure 13). Road conditions in the area are particularly bad and on many of them it is possible to travel in the dry season only and then only in vehicles with four-wheel drive. Movement away from the roads can be accomplished only with the greatest difficulty and wear-and-tear on both vehicles and personnel is very heavy. About fifty per cent of the working time of spraying teams was taken up in transporting themselves and their equipment. In the wet season conditions are very much worse. Much of the project area is located on grey 'cotton' soils, which become so plastic and sticky when they are wet that the roads are impassable for motor vehicles of any kind and they are officially closed. River transport is affected by flooding and the only mechanical means of surface transport is by the fortnightly train service from Sennar to the railhead at Er Roseires. Areas south of Er Roseires are accessible only by light aeroplane to a landing strip at Kurmuk on the Ethiopian border. In these southern parts of the project area the wet season lasts from the end of April until early November, and even after the rains have stopped some time elapses before the roads are passable and they are opened again to vehicles. Transport conditions which are comparable to, and even worse than, these are found elsewhere throughout the Sudan.

Various types of population movements take place within the project area and between it and adjacent areas. The most important movements are those of nomadic pastoralists, who make up between fifteen and twenty per cent of the total population, about the average percentage for this group for the whole of the Sudan. The nomads are an important source of malaria infection and may even transport mosquito vectors among their belongings to dry areas where these would otherwise be absent. Major difficulties occur when attempting to make contact with the nomadic groups, for they tend to travel away from main routes and to make their camps in the relatively less accessible areas. The nature of their movements is such that they are in no way dependent upon the skeletal road network that exists. The general directions and timings of

C

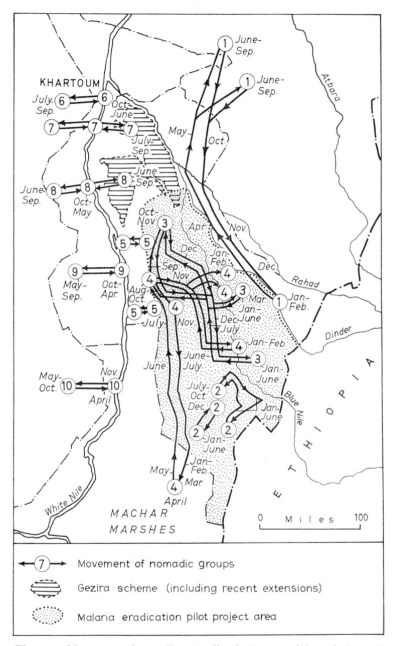

Figure 13 Movements of nomadic pastoralists in the area of the malaria eradication pilot project in Blue Nile Province, Sudan. (Based in part on a map in K. M. Barbour, *The Republic of the Sudan*, 1961.)

these movements have been determined (Figure 13) and they conform to something of a pattern. Each group tends to have its particular area for grazing and it is unusual for one group to trespass on another's pasture grounds. These elements of order and regularity are in contrast to those found among Somali pastoralists in the Horn of Africa (see page 67). When contacts have been established with nomads in Blue Nile Province they have shown themselves to be reasonably amenable to anti-malarial measures, allowing blood slides to be taken from their children and for spleen measurements to be made. One sure way of establishing friendly relations with them is by showing interest in their animals which are their main concern. In 1960 when the *nazirs*, the heads of nomadic groups, were brought to Wad Medani so that a scheme for improved health services might be outlined to them, their first question when the Provincial Medical Officer had finished speaking was, 'But you have said nothing about our animals. What is to be done for them? If they are healthy then so are we, but if they die then we die also.' Such concern is much greater than that of the cultivator for his land, and the nomad's dependence on his animals is so great that this example is not an exaggeration.

Contacts may be most easily established during the periods of the years when the nomadic groups are relatively more together than they are at other times. During the wet season they concentrate near hills of the Jebel Dali, Jebel Moya and Jebel Mazum, to cultivate a little *dura* (*Sorghum vulgare*, guinea corn). Probably only some members of each group are involved in this activity and others continue to move with the animals, but during the rains there is better grazing generally available and movements are thus less wide-ranging. In December the nomads congregate for the *hakras* (tribal meetings), which are also the occasions for various social events and for the less pleasant task of collecting taxes. These occasions would provide further opportunities for making contact with the majority of nomads, though not necessarily with all. Presumably some nomads in the Sudan, like some Fulani pastoralists in West Africa, attempt to evade tax payment and are therefore not present on these occasions.

For the period from January to March some of the nomadic groups move to the lands of the Gezira cotton-growing scheme, or to other areas of irrigated cotton cultivation alongside the White and the Blue Niles. Here they help to harvest the cotton crop and their camels are used to transport cotton from the fields to the collecting centres. They are prepared to take part in this work not only for the economic gain in the wages they earn, but also for the benefit which their animals gain from the much more favourable pasture and water conditions in the irrigated areas, during the months at the end of the dry season when these are generally in very short supply. Here again opportunities for contact present themselves, but again not all nomads come to the irrigated lands.

The willingness of some nomadic groups to work as labourers in the Gezira and also in the schemes for agricultural development in the Gash and Tokar deltas in Kassala Province is an example of how some of these people are showing tendencies to lead a less mobile life than they have done in the past. But there has been no investigation to show how far this tendency has progressed and there is certainly much variation between different groups. Progress to any new ways of life is only partial, and it affects only some of the nomads and is always slow. The changes that are taking place are unlikely to assist greatly the plans for malaria eradication. The rate might accelerate if there were an official policy of encouraging nomads to become more settled, but one does not exist. This absence is no doubt due partly to the problems inherent in the physical environment which would have to be solved in order to make possible large-scale settlement of nomadic populations. Probably also it reflects tacit recognition and acceptance by the authorities of the fact that pastoral nomads, probably more than any other people, react unfavourably to anything that involves, or which may seem to them to involve, coercion to change their traditional ways of life. But this is not meant to imply that the Sudan Government is ultra-conservative in its attitude towards development and that it is unprepared to promote changes. In other parts of the Sudan, for example among the Azande in Equatoria Province, changes in traditional ways of life have been taking place that will lead to greater economic efficiency and to important social improvements.

Some developments are likely to influence nomadic movements at least indirectly, such as the improvements in water supply which are being effected by the construction of boreholes, perennial wells and *hafirs* (small storage reservoirs). With more water available there will be less need for men and animals to move. The rate, however, at which developments are taking place on a large scale is too slow in relation to the timetable for malaria eradication for them to have much effect in reducing mobility.

Besides movements of nomadic pastoralists in the Blue Nile pilot project area, there is another important type of movement associated with the seasonal influx of labourers who come to help to harvest the cotton grown in the Gezira scheme and the recently completed extension in the Managil area, and on the smaller privately-owned schemes along the Blue Nile south of Singa. About 50,000 labourers (some of them the nomads and many of them 'Westerners') come each picking season to the original Gezira area; but there is no information yet of the labour that is attracted to the Managil extension, neither is anything known of the permanent or temporary labour employed on the private schemes some of which are more than 10,000 acres in extent.

Sample surveys have shown that malaria infections occur at considerably higher rates among these mobile elements in the population, as compared with the settled inhabitants, and that in some years there may be epidemic outbreaks among the migrants. While they are employed in picking, the migrant labourers are housed in temporary dwellings with roofs and walls of straw thatch supported on a framework of poles, and these are often sited on the lands which are under cotton. It has been demonstrated that these shelters are favourite resting places for *A. gambiae* and are therefore a threat to the success of anti-malarial measures unless they are treated. It is difficult to include them in the normal cycles of insecticide spraying, either because of the problem of finding them or because they are erected after the spray teams have been at work. Even when they can be found they are difficult to treat effectively, for the materials from which they are constructed do not adequately retain insecticides.

Besides these major movements of population in which large numbers of people are involved, there are also much smaller and more localized movements of people which may also influence malaria and its eradication. The southern boundary of the Blue Nile pilot project area, between Gheisan and Kurmuk, runs for some distance along the international boundary between the Sudan and Ethiopia. This is very wild country and only sparsely populated, with between two and ten persons per square mile and with large areas that are uninhabited. It is impossible to envisage how people moving in this area could be controlled, particularly those who cross from the Sudan to Ethiopia and vice versa. At Gheisan, for instance, the boundary between the two countries is a river, the Khor Tomat, which is seasonal in its flow and for many months of the year a fifty-yard walk across its dry sandy bed means crossing between the Sudan and Ethiopia without hindrance. Even when it is flowing the *khor* is no barrier to movement. At Kurmuk there are no natural features which define the international boundary and movements across it take place for the most part freely. But some of the movements by night are clandestine, for people cross into Ethiopia to drink *arragi*, a distilled spirit which along with other forms of alcohol is forbidden in the Muslim Sudan. Those who travel for this illicit purpose do so at times when mosquito activity is at a maximum and there is every likelihood of them being bitten.

There is some evidence to show that movements such as these affect the malaria situation on the Sudanese side of the boundary by the continual introduction of fresh infections from Ethiopia. In 1960 an epidemic of yellow fever in Ethiopia was certainly spread in this way into this part of the Sudan. Any control of movements is out of the question, and the only adequate solution to the problems that they create would lie in the possibility of establishing comparable and coordinated programmes for eradication in both countries. Some moves have been made towards establishing liaison in malaria work between the Sudan and Ethiopia, though whether this could lead to simultaneous and concentrated action in the near future is doubtful. The parts of Ethiopia adjacent to the Blue Nile and Upper Nile Province are inaccessible and poorly developed; they are remote from Addis Ababa and communications with the capital by land are very difficult and for much of the time they are non-existent. It would certainly not be easy for the Ethiopian authorities to mount a malaria eradication scheme here. Indeed, it could be argued that one could be more effectively directed and controlled from the Sudan than from Ethiopia. At the same time it is certain that such a degree of international cooperation as would make this feasible will not be achieved in the foreseeable future.

The various movements of population which have been outlined in Blue Nile Province and in other parts of the Sudan are liable to cross and recross one another to produce intricate and confused patterns. The complexity of the annual movements of people through a district of Kassala Province has been described as follows:

> During June as the Westerners who have been working in the Gezira cotton schemes are returning to their villages in Southern Gedaref, to the north the Shukriya from Rufa's are seen coming with their animals for summer grazing – intermingling with their fellow tribesmen who are also beginning to move northwards. In July and August the Rufa'a el Sharg enter from the south-west, grazing their camels along the way as they are joined by the nomadic Kenana and Kawahla in the Butana. A little later the Rufa'a el Hoi from near the Ingessana hills enter from the south, and the Blue Nile Kenana and Kawahla from the west, all on the way to the same broad grazing

area. During October and November one notices the Beni'Amer, Hadendowa and the fair-skinned Bashaida coming from the north-east of the Atbara to find grazing in the region of Kashm el Girba. From December onwards the Westerners are off again to the cotton schemes in the Gezira and the movement back of the nomadic tribesmen begins. . . .*

This description of movements is given only in the broadest terms, and to complete the picture of mobility in this part of the Sudan further information on other mobile elements would have to be added. A full assessment of these movements and of others elsewhere in the Sudan can come only from detailed work in the field applied specifically to this task. There is certainly an element of seasonal rhythm in many of the movements but this may change significantly from year to year with minor variations in environmental conditions. The timings of move-ments may change and so may the routes along which they take place. None of those which have been described is likely to come to an end in the near future. The general prospects for nomadic pastoralism have already been discussed. Migrant agricultural labour is likely to increase in amount with the already completed Managil extension in the Gezira and will increase further with the completion of a new dam on the Blue Nile at Damasin, a few miles upstream from Er Roseires. The latter will make water available for gravity-fed irrigation to extend areas under cultivation in lands south of the existing Gezira scheme. Develop-ments on a smaller scale in the Gash and Tokar deltas already attract migrant labour and they are likely to continue doing so. With an ever-increasing amount of conversion to Islam in West Africa, coupled with improvements in means of transport, the number of pilgrims will in-crease rather than diminish. As one of the major Muslim countries in Africa the Sudan is unlikely to wish to impede in any way the move-ments of fellow Muslims through the country *en route* to and from Mecca.

Together these movements certainly provide the greatest variety in mobility and probably involve the greatest number of people in any African state. All are likely to influence the progress of malaria eradica-tion in the Sudan. They may well prejudice its success unless measures are taken to deal with them adequately in the eradication programme. To design these measures it is necessary in the first instance to accumulate much more data on mobility than has previously been

* D. B. Climenhaga in *The Population of Sudan: Report of the Sixth Annual Conference of the Philosophical Society of Sudan*, Khartoum, 1958.

available and to evaluate fully the relationships between mobile and static elements in the population. These were among the tasks of the pre-eradication surveys which were made during the period from 1961 to 1963. It is in the attack phase which follows these surveys that complications will arise from the mobile elements and these will add significantly to the cost of operations, in terms of money and of personnel, both of which are in short supply in the Sudan. As the first of the large and highly malarious countries in Africa to reach this stage in its progress towards malaria eradication it will be most interesting and revealing to observe what success the Sudanese are able to achieve in tackling these problems. The effort they are making is a very brave one and the experience that will be gained from it will provide much valuable information for dealing with comparable situations elsewhere in the continent.

BIBLIOGRAPHY

K. M. Barbour, *The Republic of the Sudan: a Regional Geography*, 1961, provides all the essential information, and much of the detail, on the physical environment, the population and economic and social development. Further details on the population of the Sudan, including information on mobility, are given in K. J. Krotki, *First Population Census of Sudan 1955/56: 21 Facts about the Sudanese*, Khartoum, 1958; *The Population of Sudan: Report of the Sixth Annual Conference of the Philosophical Society of Sudan*, Khartoum, 1958; D. B. Mather, 'Migration in the Sudan', in R. W. Steel and C. A. Fisher (*ed.*), *Geographical Essays on British Tropical Lands*, 1956; I. A. Hassoun, 'Western Migration and Settlement in the Gezira', *Sudan Notes and Records*, **33**, 1952; H. R. J. Davies, 'The West African in the Economic Geography of Sudan', *Geography*, **49**, 1964, 222; I. Cunnison, 'The Humr and their Land', *Sudan Notes and Records*, **35**, 1954, 50; Sudan Government, *The Equatorial Nile Project and its Effects on the Anglo-Egyptian Sudan, Report of the Jonglei Investigation Team*, Khartoum, 1954, and *Natural Resources and Development Potential in the Southern Provinces of the Sudan, Report of the Southern Development Investigation Team*, Khartoum, 1954.

5 The Horn of Africa

THE Horn of Africa includes the Ethiopian Federation, the Republic of Somalia, the north-eastern parts of Kenya, and the small colonial enclave of French Somaliland. In the Ethiopian Federation is the former Italian colony of Eritrea which was joined in 1950 with Ethiopia, the oldest of the independent states of Africa. By contrast its neighbour, the Republic of Somalia, is one of the new independent African countries, having come into being with the union of the former Somaliland Protectorate (British Somaliland) and the former United Nations Trust Territory of Somalia (previously Italian Somaliland) on 1 July 1960. Parts of the Northern Frontier Province of Kenya have both geographical and ethnic affinities with Somalia to the north-east and they differ from the rest of the country of which they are a part. Kenya gained its independence from Britain in 1963, and so French Somaliland is now the only colonial territory in North-east Africa. Small and isolated, its economy is dependent very largely on the railway which links its capital and port, Djibouti, with Addis Ababa, and provides Ethiopia's main surface transport link with the outside world. Its southern neighbour, the Republic of Somalia, wishes to incoporate it, together with the eastern parts of Ethiopia and parts of the Northern Frontier Province of Kenya, within a greater nation state that will unite and include all Somali people.

The problems of malaria eradication in the Horn of Africa are related to inadequate data and the difficulties of obtaining them, and to highly mobile nomadic populations and the political difficulties which arise from their movements when these involve the crossing of international boundaries. Here pastoralism and politics combine to prejudice the progress of public health.

Problems of data

Although it is the oldest of independent African states, Ethiopia remains a country about which very little is known, particularly in terms of quantitative data relating to its area and to the numbers, the structure and the economic and social characteristics of its population. Much of its area of 500,000 square miles is difficult terrain of well-watered high plateaux cut by deep river valleys, with steep escarpments and extensive semi-arid lowlands. These features make communications difficult and have resulted in the isolation of one part of the country from another.

For centuries Ethiopia has been subject to feudal forms of government, with its various parts subject to little direct central administrative control. These parts have developed and still maintain a considerable degree of individuality and independence. Travel to some parts of the country is still officially restricted, quite apart from difficulties of movement arising from the absence of transport other than on foot or on horseback. With this combination of difficult environmental, administrative and social factors it is hardly surprising that there is little information of any sort available, and that it has been virtually impossible to obtain quantitative data.

Ethiopia is one of the few parts of Africa in which no census of population has yet been taken and therefore the estimate of the total population at about 20 million is based largely on intelligent guesswork. Any more specific data, on the structure of the population, on details of its distribution, on changes in its composition and on its mobility, are almost completely lacking. In many other parts of Africa, even before it was possible to organize a census of the population, data could be estimated from the numbers of adult males who paid tax and these estimates were used extensively and successfully. Unfortunately this method of estimation cannot be applied in Ethiopia where tax is paid not on a per capita basis but on land, and the amount that has to be paid is determined by the percentage of land under cultivation.

The organization of a census in Ethiopia would be difficult, if only because of an insufficient number of literate enumerators to take it, and the success of any census is dependent upon the efficient collection of data at the lowest, but nonetheless the most important, level of the census organization. The difficulties that would have to be faced by census enumerators during their work in the field – poor communications and a dispersed population in difficult terrain – are probably as great as anywhere in Africa. At the same time the administrative hierarchy that exists in the country should facilitate the organization of a census. It is composed of units which range from provinces down to small areas; the latter vary in size but generally contain from 100 to 150 families. Each of these small units has a headman who controls the group and is conversant with its affairs. These units might well be made the basis for the lowest but most important unit of census enumeration.

Malaria eradication pilot projects

The absence of basic population data hinders the making of any accurate assessment of the incidence and effects of diseases. Without these data it is difficult to envisage planning the logistics of any countrywide programme for eradicating malaria. So far in Ethiopia it has been possible to carry out only pilot projects for malaria eradication, which have been restricted in the areas and in the populations covered. But even in these small schemes problems have arisen from the lack of data and other information. In the pilot project in the Awash valley, to the east of Addis Ababa, it was impossible to obtain complete coverage in spraying operations because of the dispersed settlement, with dwellings often scattered in thick bush cover, and because of failure to understand semi-nomadic population movements which caused frequent changes in the location of dwellings. Such circumstances, though they will complicate the task of eradication, can be assessed, and attempts can be made to deal with them if efficient geographical reconnaissance is carried out at the planning stage of the eradication programme. This reconnaissance must then be maintained throughout the programme in order to take account of changes that may result from movements of population and from other factors.

The conditions of the physical and human environments represented in the pilot project in the Awash valley, and in another centred on Gondar, were comparatively favourable and above the average for what might be expected in much of Ethiopia. From the point of view of the logistics of the eradication programmes, communications in both project areas were relatively good, allowing a considerable employment of motor vehicles, whose use is very limited in most parts of Ethiopia. As a result little experience was gained in the use of animal transport, by mule and donkey, on which much of a countrywide eradication programme would have to depend. These pilot projects, therefore, can hardly be said to have provided entirely fair tests of the problems that would be encountered in eradication throughout Ethiopia.

The 1958 malaria epidemic

General surveys have shown that malaria is widespread throughout Ethiopia and that eradication measures would need to be applied to about fifty per cent of the population. Altitude sets certain limits upon the incidence of the disease and at heights of 6,000 feet and above there is little malaria in endemic form. The populations of these higher areas, therefore, are highly susceptible to infection and they are liable to be affected by regional epidemics. These epidemics are usually of minor proportions, but in 1958 a highly populated area of over 100,000 square miles was affected by a severe epidemic of malaria which lasted from the end of June until the middle of December. It caused high rates of morbidity and mortality among people who had not been subjected to serious malaria infection for more than a decade.

Table 4 Malaria cases diagnosed and treated in ten hospitals in Ethiopia in 1958, compared with the average for previous years for which records were available.

Hospital	1958	Average for previous years
Debra Tabor	2,780	126
Debra Zeit	4,094	948
Jimma	670	186
Soddo	1,348	713
Lekemt	4,366	2,070
Addis Ababa (5 hospitals)	2,512	no data

The figures in the table above give only some indication of the situation, for in a country like Ethiopia with only a skeletal hospital service, only a very small minority of cases who may require hospital treatment are able to receive it.

Though it was impossible to assess accurately the magnitude of the epidemic and its effects, it was conservatively estimated that there were between three million and three and a half million cases of malaria, with the number of deaths amounting to 150,000. Mortality is known to have been as high as twenty-five per cent in parts of Shoa and Gojjam Provinces whose populations were also suffering from a famine resulting from harvest failures in 1957. With lowered resistance because of undernutrition, the inhabitants of these areas readily succumbed to malaria. Even in areas which were not so seriously affected the epidemic disrupted normal life, and in parts of the valley of the Blue Nile in October 1958 it was reported, 'there are not enough healthy individuals remaining to fetch water for the sick. Many people are dying. . . . The crops which are unattended for lack of guards are being destroyed by baboons, wild pigs, birds and other wild life.'

The immediate causes of the epidemic were the increased breeding of the main mosquito vector, *A. gambiae*, and accelerated development of the malaria parasite. The greater numbers of vectors were due to the abnormal weather experienced in Ethiopia in 1958 when rainfall, temperature and humidity in the highland provinces, where the epidemic was most severe, were higher than for previous years for which records were available. It is probable that the distribution of the rainfall was more important than the actual amounts which fell; rain fell for a more extended period of the year than was usual and in appreciable quantities in months that are usually dry. These conditions favoured increased numbers of mosquitoes, prolonged their lives and permitted them to disperse over much greater areas than is usual. Together with a reservoir of infection and a large susceptible human population these factors precipitated the outbreaks of malaria in epidemic proportions. The concurrence of similar conditions has been recorded as the cause of a major regional epidemic in India in 1929.

Somali pastoralism

While the majority of the people of Ethiopia are sedentary cultivators the Somali people are nomadic pastoralists *par excellence*. They form a homogeneous ethnic group, speaking the same language and further united by their adherence to Islam, which is distributed over large areas of the Horn of Africa. Having originated in the Arabian peninsula they have spread out during the last centuries to occupy the whole of what is now the independent Republic of Somalia, parts of French Somaliland, Ethiopia and northern Kenya. This distribution has been achieved by an almost imperceptible migratory drift of people, movements which were still continuing during the first three decades of the present century when the Somali spread south of the Juba river and into the Northern Frontier Province of Kenya. They were finally halted, roughly along the line of the Tana river, only by the application of strict measures by the Kenya authorities in the 1930s.

This migratory drift is only one element in the mobility of the majority of the Somali people whose lives are fundamentally influenced by the relatively harsh physical environment in which they live. Low rainfall, which is unreliable in amount and incidence and is concentrated into short periods of the year with correspondingly long dry periods, greatly restricts the possibilities of livelihood. Cultivation can take place only in very limited areas and a pastoral life with camels, sheep and goats is the only one that is possible for the majority of the Somali. Furthermore, pasture and water are so scarce that they must wander for much of the year with their herds and flocks in search of these necessities, and they are even forced to compete with one another for the limited amounts that are available. Besides the prime need to move in search of pasture and water, the seasonal migrations of people and animals are influenced by relationships between groups of pastoralists, the incidence of stock and human diseases and administrative direction when this can be enforced.

More than eighty-five per cent of the population in Northern Somalia (formerly British Somaliland) is nomadic, and sixty-five per cent in Southern Somalia (formerly United Nations Trust Territory). The smaller proportion of nomads in the latter reflects the relatively higher rainfall in the south, the presence of permanent water in the Juba and Webe Shebelli rivers which rise on the well-watered Ethiopian Plateau, and the presence in the population of elements who are not Somali and who by tradition are cultivators and not pastoralists. Somali nomads are disdainful of cultivators and regard them as inferior, and this attitude, in addition to the harsh physical environment, militates against such limited economic development as might be possible. This would be mainly in the south where during Italian colonial rule Italian enterprise and capital were responsible for the development of about 25,000 acres just south of Mogadishu, mainly growing bananas. A survey carried out in 1960 indicated possibilities for irrigating a further 500,000 acres in the southern parts of the country.

Northern Somalia (Figures 14 and 15)

The problems of the nomadic way of life of the Somali and their relevance to malaria and its eradication are best illustrated in Northern Somalia. Here, during the main dry season of the year, which lasts from November to March, the majority of the nomads are forced to concentrate with their stock within range of the sources of permanent water that are to be found in their home wells at places like Hargeisa, Odweina, Burao, Ainabo and Los Anod. In the course of time this has resulted in over-grazing and deterioration of the pastures near these places, and they are unable to support the stock throughout the year. Thus with the onset of the main Gu rains in April people and stock begin to move southward to the Haud, a great rolling plateau area with little relief, ranging from 4,000–2,000 feet above sea-level and covering an area of about 50,000 square miles. In the dry season the Haud is waterless, and persistent geological investigations have failed to reveal sources of underground water at depths at which it could be exploited. But when the rains fall the grass grows and the shallow depressions on the plateau surface fill up with water, though only to be rapidly depleted not only from consumption by people and stock but also through loss due to high rates of evaporation.

The occurrence of water and pasture even during the wet season is scattered and unpredictable, because of the sporadic nature of the rainfall both in time and space. Rain falls in violent storms of short duration and with very high intensity. Within a few minutes of its onset the

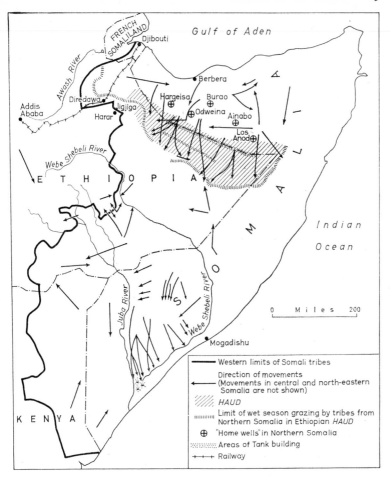

Figure 14 Movements of Somali pastoralists in the Horn of Africa. (Based on maps by the author in *Bulletin, World Health Organization, Geographical Journal* and Steel and Prothero, *op. cit.*)

area affected by a storm is flooded, there is very considerable water loss through uncontrollable run-off and both sheet erosion and gully erosion are common. Each storm affects a limited area of only a few square miles. In 1960, when the *Gu* rains commenced several weeks earlier than usual, and when some parts of Somaliland were experiencing serious floods, it was possible to spend several days in the Haud without once actually being rained upon. Continually round and about, within distances of only a few miles, rain could be seen falling.

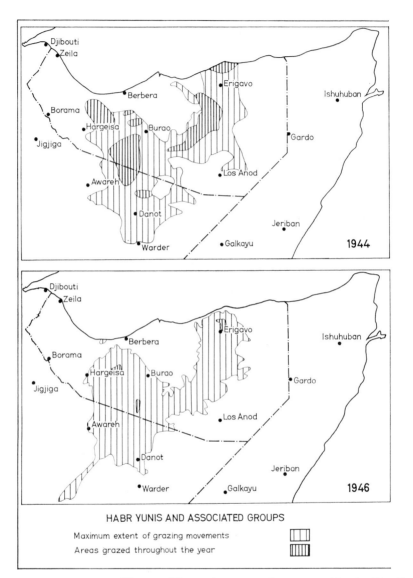

HABR YUNIS AND ASSOCIATED GROUPS

Maximum extent of grazing movements

Areas grazed throughout the year

Figure 15 The varying extent of areas grazed by the Habr Yunis,
A Survey of Somaliland Protectorate 1951, and

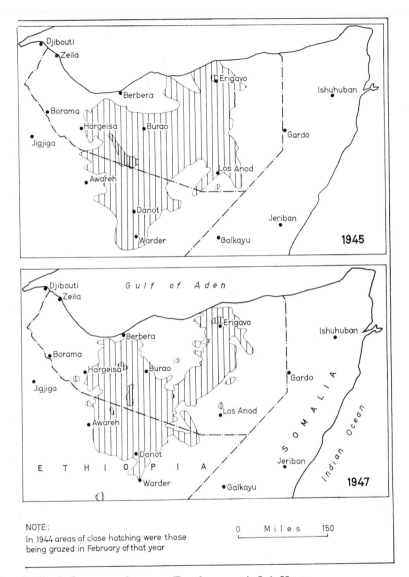

NOTE:
In 1944 areas of close hatching were those
being grazed in February of that year

0   M i l e s   150

a Somali tribe, in four successive years. (Based on maps in J. A. Hunt,
a map by the author in *Geographical Journal*.)

The main aim in life for the nomads and their animals is to move as rapidly as possible to areas where rain has fallen, to graze there until the grass is exhausted, and then to move on to new pastures. Leaders of the various nomadic groups, using their local knowledge allied with great intuition, take their people and animals to the most favourable grazing areas. Scouts are employed to range out in search of these and it has been said that those representing different groups 'lie scientifically' to one another, so that they may obtain the best pasture and water for their own people and deny it to others.* No precise rights can be defined to pasture and water when conditions are so precarious and are always changing. Disputes often arise between groups over rights to these precious necessities and they frequently lead to violence.

Not only is the environment unpredictable, making necessary the mass movement of people and animals, but the composition of nomadic groups is also constantly changing. The size of each group is small, consisting usually of several families which form a *rer*. These families may move together for some time and then disperse, some to join other *rer*, or themselves to be joined by families from other *rer*. The process is one of continual fission and fusion.

Somali nomads maintain themselves with the minimum of equipment and personal belongings, with dwellings (*akal*) that can be easily erected and dismantled. Each *akal* consists of a framework of branches covered with mats, cloth or skins, and usually a combination of these, and is roughly hemispherical in shape. Setting up and striking camp is women's work, and these tasks are accomplished by them with incredible speed. Within an hour a *rer* can be away from one camp site and may move up to a hundred miles in the course of the next sixty hours to a new area where pasture and water have been reported. As pasture and water become progressively more scarce, for the main rains last only from April until June, the young men range farther afield than the rest of the nomadic groups in search of grazing for the camels which are able to go for periods of at least twenty days without water. During these extended movements they live under excessively harsh conditions without any shelter, on a monotonous though nutritious diet of camel's milk only and without water for themselves. They are able generally to judge their return, leaving only the smallest margin of safety, but occasionally judgments are incorrect or other factors intervene and animals die and even human lives may be lost.

The time that can be spent grazing in the Haud is prolonged by the secondary *Dhair* rains which fall in September and October. But as

* J. A. Hunt, *A General Survey of Somaliland Protectorate 1944–50*, 1951.

their effect diminishes the tribes are forced to retreat to the sources of permanent water at the home wells and the annual cycle of their movements is completed. The nomadic population is at greatest risk to malaria infection during the wet season in the Haud, when the areas of open water which form with the rains provide breeding grounds for the few mosquitoes that are able to survive the aridity of the dry season. A sharp increase takes place in the number of vectors, with consequent accelerating rates in the transmission of malaria. The disease strikes in epidemic form since at other times in the year the people are not subject to infection. In 1961 abnormally heavy and prolonged rains over much of East and North-east Africa not only caused severe losses of stock and crops through flooding, but also produced an epidemic of malaria of very considerable proportions, particularly in the southern parts of Somalia.

Water supplies and malaria

Conditions which are favourable for maintained and increased breeding of mosquitoes have developed in recent years as a result of measures taken to improve water supplies in the Haud. Owing to the absence of perennial streams and underground supplies which can be exploited, the only possibility for improvement lies in conserving water during the meagre rains of the wet season, by preventing some of the losses which occur through uncontrolled run-off during the storms and subsequent evaporation. Natural depressions in the ground have been deepened to form shallow reservoirs called *balleh*, but the amount of water that can be collected in them is small and is quickly depleted through use and by high evaporation losses. Much more efficient means of water storage are the tanks which have been constructed during recent years. Excavations are made to greater depths than with the *balleh* and they are then lined with stone masonry and cement to prevent water seepage, and are also roofed with sheets of corrugated iron and with brushwood to reduce evaporation. The capacities of the tanks vary from 20,000 to over 100,000 gallons. Each tank is sited to take advantage of natural run-off, but to assist the collection of maximum amounts of water channels are also dug to converge on the tank from all parts of the catchment in which it is located. The tanks have been built by private enterprise and, with normal charges of four shillings for forty-four gallons rising to as much as eighteen shillings for the same amount in times of shortage, they are a profitable venture. When they were built first they were sited along either side of the Ethiopian–Somalia boundary; more recently they have been located at distances of fifty miles or more from the boundary down in the Ethiopian section of the Haud.

People and stock are now able to remain in the Haud for much longer than was previously possible before having to move back to the home wells, with a consequent reduction in the amount of over-grazing on the lands near the sources of permanent water. At the same time the new water supplies have introduced new problems. The tanks especially have proved to be ideal breeding places for mosquitoes and breeding can now continue into the dry season in areas where formerly this was not possible; consequently the length of the season of transmission of malaria has been increased. The longer periods that the nomads can now spend in the Haud have also added to the political problems which bedevil the lands occupied by the Somali people and these, in their turn, exercise an important influence upon public health.

Pastoralism and politics

Like so many other ethnic groups in Africa the Somali were victims of boundary delimitation by the European powers in their scrambles for colonial territories at the end of the nineteenth century and in the early years of the present century. Though they have achieved some measure of unification with the formation of the independent Republic of Somalia in 1960, the Somali are still divided among four territories. Already the Republic has provided a focus for aspirations to unite all Somali under one national flag and to incorporate those lands outside the Republic where they form a majority in the population. Pan-Somalia ideals, naturally, are anathema to the adjacent countries with these Somali groups.

Relations are most difficult between Somalia and Ethiopia, for not only do about half a million Somali live permanently in the Ogaden Province of Ethiopia, but there is also the seasonal incursion of nomadic groups into the country from Northern Somalia. The boundary that is crossed in these movements, between Ethiopia and the former British Protectorate of Somaliland, was defined and delimited in an Anglo-Ethiopian treaty of 1897. The treaty was made at a time when Britain was under pressure in other parts of North-east Africa, thus giving Ethiopia some advantage in the negotiations, and the boundary was defined so that large areas occupied by Somalis came under Ethiopian rule. Furthermore, it divided the grazing area of the Haud so that the greater part came into Ethiopian territory. The Somalis from the north have no alternative but to use the whole of the Haud to graze their animals during the wet season and their rights to do this were recognized and protected in the treaty. These rights were reaffirmed in an agreement made between Britain and Ethiopia in 1954 when the Ogaden

Province was returned to Ethiopia, bringing to an end the British Military Administration in North-east Africa. Under this Administration, which was set up in 1942 after the defeat of the Italian forces in Northeast Africa, the Somalis enjoyed a greater measure of unity than they had had before or have had since. From 1942 to 1948 Italian Somaliland, Somaliland Protectorate and the Ethiopian Ogaden were jointly administered and an abortive attempt was made by Britain after the war to arrange a permanent solution of Somali problems on this basis. In 1948, after the failure of these efforts, Somaliland Protectorate once more came under British colonial administration, Italian Somaliland became a United Nations Trust Territory in 1950, and in 1954 the Ogaden Province was returned to Ethiopia. Understandably, the Somali have never been satisfied with the ways in which they are divided, or with their somewhat tenuous grazing rights in the Haud. Since the independence of the Republic of Somalia relations with Ethiopia have been severely strained, with continual tension along the boundary and periodic outbreaks of violence between the nationals of the two countries.

Politics and public health

The unfavourable consequences for malaria of improvements in the water supplies in the Haud have already been indicated, though it is possible to treat the water in the tanks with briquettes impregnated with chemicals to prevent mosquito breeding, without fouling the water for drinking by either man or animals. But this method is effective only if all tanks are treated. In the period immediately before the independence of the Republic of Somalia the tanks which lined either side of the boundary between Somaliland Protectorate and Ethiopia were being treated in the former territory but not in the latter. While therefore an attempt was being made to control vector breeding in Somaliland Protectorate, less than 100 yards distant across the boundary breeding was able to continue without interruption. Mosquitoes do not respect international boundaries and the efforts that were being made in the one territory were only being frustrated by the lack of any effort in the other. Even if there were some way of excluding infected mosquitoes coming from Ethiopia there are the annual movements of hundreds of thousands of Somali nomads into Ethiopia for several months of the year, during which time they are exposed to malaria infection in the Haud. With the extension of tank building in recent years further south in the Ethiopian section of the Haud there are presumably still further opportunities for increased mosquito breeding.

Several attempts have been made to bring about a united effort against malaria by the countries in the Horn of Africa. They have failed because of political tension and resulting suspicion. Without a common effort, particularly in view of such a high degree of population mobility, there is little prospect of eradicating malaria from this part of the continent. The lack of cooperation and understanding has been such that even personnel of the World Health Organization working in Somaliland Protectorate in 1960 were not permitted to pursue their malaria investigations across into Ethiopia. Until the unification of Somaliland Protectorate and the United Nations Trust Territory of Somalia the former was an isolated enclave of the African Region of the World Health Organization, because of the political links which it had with other British territories in East Africa; Somalia together with Ethiopia were parts of the W.H.O. Eastern Mediterranean Region. This anomaly certainly did not help the problem of developing international co-operation between the three countries. Since the formation of the independent Republic of Somalia, however, the whole of North-east Africa is now part of the Eastern Mediterranean Region (see Frontispiece map).

Pastoralism and public health

Among a highly mobile population, composed of groups whose composition is continually changing, conditions are ideal for the transmission of disease. In the nomadic encampments people live in close contact with one another and tuberculosis is rampant among the Somali. Even if international cooperation can be achieved, the problems of dealing in a programme of malaria eradication with a population of whom the majority are nomadic remain to be solved. Contacts with these people, for regular spraying of their encampments, for the diagnosis of malaria infections, and for the distribution of drugs, are very difficult to establish and maintain. Permanent centres for treatment are of little use for there can be no assured population within their range for them to serve. In the latter part of the 1950s experiments were carried out with prefabricated dispensaries which could be easily erected and dismantled like the nomad dwellings. They were moved around and set up in areas where at a particular time there were large concentrations of nomads. In an effort to get people to use the dispensaries and to understand something of the medical facilities available, selected members of nomadic groups were given a brief elementary training in first-aid and hygiene. This was intended to be sufficient to enable them to give a certain amount of first-aid themselves and then to direct those requiring more expert attention to dispensaries and hospitals. These measures have had some success in breaking down the barriers of reticence and suspicion that exist with a conservative and strongly individualistic people like the pastoral Somali. Certainly until very recent times they have always resented and have rebuffed any attempts to apply measures that might seem to interfere with them and with their way of life, even if these were intended to confer what might seem to others to be obvious benefits. General public health education, which is the usual means of explaining the importance and advantages of medical measures, is difficult to organize among people for whom it has not yet been possible to devise and apply a satisfactory system of elementary education, though several investigations have been made of the problems involved.

Ethiopia and the lands of the Somali people in the Horn of Africa are among the most backward economically in the whole continent. Most parts of the Ethiopian plateau offer possibilities for economic development, provided that the necessary capital and technical knowledge can be made available. But in those parts of the Horn of Africa inhabited by the Somali the environment is harsh and the economic potential in the foreseeable future is poor. The areas suitable for crop cultivation are very limited, and prospecting has revealed no large quantities of economic minerals. Pastoral nomadism is thus likely to remain for a long time the means of livelihood for the majority of Somali people, and to meet the circumstances of the environment they have no alternative but to undertake an annual cycle of movements with their stock. They, and the sedentary peoples with whom they come into contact, will continue to be ravaged by malaria and other diseases until adequate interterritorial coordination and cooperation are established to achieve eradication. It should not be beyond the bounds of possibility to organize these among reasonable people. Unfortunately the Horn of Africa provides only one of the many examples in the continent where a preparedness to work together is lacking, though it illustrates some of the most difficult problems that may arise under these circumstances.

BIBLIOGRAPHY

Malaria in the Horn of Africa is surveyed generally in D. Bagster Wilson et al., 'Malaria in Abyssinia', East African Medical Journal, 22, 1945, 285, and D. Bagster Wilson, 'Malaria in British Somaliland', *ibid.*, **26**, 1949, 283, and in much greater detail for Somalia in R. Choumara, 'Notes sur le Paludisme au Somaliland', *Rivista di Malariologia*, **38**, 1960, 21, and M. Maffi, 'La Malaria nelle Regioni del Mudughe della Migiurtania, Somalia', *Rivista di Malariologia*, **40**, 1960, 9. E. Ullendorf, *The Ethiopians*, 1960, provides a general background to the country. The pastoral nomads of Northern Somalia have been studied in great detail by I. M. Lewis, *A Pastoral Democracy; a Study of Pastoralism and Politics among the Northern Somali of the Horn of Africa*, 1961; see also, by the same author, 'Modern Political Movements in Somaliland', *Africa*, **28**, 1958, 244 and 344. Details of ecological conditions in former British Somaliland are to be found in J. A. Hunt, *A General Survey of Somaliland Protectorate, 1944–50*, Hargeisa, 1951. Somalia's claims in the Horn of Africa are set forth in great detail and with remarkable objectivity by the Somali Information Services in *The Somali Peninsula*, Mogadishu, 1962; J. G. Drysdale, *The Somali Dispute*, 1963. See also, A. Odone, 'Somalia's Economy: Prospects and Problems', *Civilisations*, **11**, 1961, 444, and C. Bonnani, 'Literacy for Nomads in Somalia', *Overseas Education*, **33**, 1961, 88.

6 East and South-central Africa

SEDENTARY cultivation is dominant in the indigenous economics of East and South-central Africa, though there are also some groups of nomadic and semi-nomadic pastoralists – the Karamojong in north-eastern Uganda, the Somali, Galla, Turkana and Masai in Kenya, with the last of these spreading over into northern Tanganyika. By comparison with nomadic pastoralists in Somalia, and even in the Sudan, their numbers are small. They are only a small proportion of the total population of East Africa but they are widely distributed and with their animals they range over vast areas of country – over about three-quarters of Kenya and over one-quarter of the whole of East Africa. Their movements will almost certainly have some influence on the progress of malaria eradication when this is undertaken on a large scale, but no investigation of the likely nature of this influence has yet been made. Partly for this reason, and also because in general their ways of life are similar to those of nomadic groups in the Sudan, Ethiopia and Somalia with whom they have ethnic affinities, the East African pastoralists are not discussed here. They are likely to present problems which are comparable to those which have been outlined in the two previous chapters. Except for the Masai, whose lands are adjacent to areas occupied by sedentary cultivators, some differences may result from the fact that many of the East African pastoralists live in areas that are remote from settled populations, and they therefore have little contact with them as compared, for example, with nomads in Blue Nile Province.

Labour migration

The population movements in East Africa which demand particular attention are those associated with the migrant labourers who travel long distances, both within and between East African territories and beyond to the Rhodesias and to the Republic of South Africa. The magnitude of their movements and their importance for malaria eradication have been underestimated, and there is some tendency to believe that they can either easily be controlled or that adequate checks can be made on them. In practice neither of these is likely to be possible except to a very limited extent.

Though some tribes were already involved in limited labour movements at the end of the nineteenth century the main movements of migrant labourers have developed during the last sixty years. The volume of migrants has grown steadily in response to demands for labour from economic enterprises developed mainly through direct or indirect European influence.

Table 5 Estimates of numbers of migrant labourers in East, South-central and South Africa in the mid-1950s

From	To	Number of migrants
Ruanda-Urundi, Tanganyika		
Kenya, Belgian Congo, Sudan	Uganda	74,000
Tanganyika	N. Rhodesia	6,000
	Union of S. Africa	15,000
N. Rhodesia	S. Rhodesia	100,000
	Union of S. Africa	42,000
	Other territories	8,000
Moçambique	Union of S. Africa	164,000
	S. Rhodesia	157,000
Bechuanaland	Union of S. Africa	21,000
Swaziland	Union of S. Africa	9,000
Ruanda-Urundi, Moçambique,		
N. Rhodesia, Kenya, Nyasaland	Tanganyika	50,000
Countries unspecified	Kenya	14,000

Source: International Labour Office, Geneva.

The numbers above total 655,000, but were certainly underestimated, and in any case the large outflow of migrant labourers from Nyasaland to Southern Rhodesia and the Union of South Africa was not given, nor was any attempt made to assess the volume of movements within countries. In Tanganyika, for example, internal movements are considerable and the number of migrants amounts to more than 300,000 each year. Migrant numbers may fluctuate enormously from year to year; in 1946, for instance, 140,000 migrants were estimated to have left Ruanda-Urundi alone for Uganda. Since the time when the I.L.O. figures were compiled various changes in East and South-central Africa have affected the movements of migrants, particularly the political changes consequent on the achievement of independence by several countries. Disturbed conditions in the Congo and in the new republics of Rwanda and Burundi have resulted in the movements of refugees into Uganda. They have also come into Uganda from the southern provinces of the Sudan. The attitudes of independent African countries towards the racial policies pursued by the Republic of South Africa and by Portugal in Africa have resulted in some lessening in the flow of migrant labourers to South Africa and from Angola and Moçambique. The Tanganyika Government no longer permits recruiting by the Witwatersrand Native Labour Association among the Nyakyusa people in the Southern Highlands Province.

Differential rates of migration

There is considerable variation in the tendency to migrate among the different tribes in East Africa, and this feature has been noted elsewhere in the continent. If it is possible, when planning a malaria eradication programme, to pinpoint those areas from which movements are taking place, particular attention can be paid to them and detailed investigation can be undertaken to establish the features of mobility. A useful but simple means of calculating the rates of migration of different tribes has been applied to data from the censuses of Tanganyika (1948 and 1957), Kenya (1948) and Uganda (1948). In this method the number of persons in a tribe living in its home district was subtracted from the total figure for the tribe recorded in the census; the result was then expressed as a percentage of the total number of the tribe and was called the *emigration rate*.

Between the different tribes the rates vary considerably, the differences having been caused by various factors. For instance, the Karamojong in the remote and inaccessible parts of north-eastern Uganda are almost completely untouched by modern forms of population mobility. Few of them move any great distances from their tribal area, though as nomadic pastoralists they are mobile within it. In contrast, the Kikuyu in Kenya have high emigration rates, though their movements from Kikuyuland have been largely restricted to other parts of Kenya and very few have gone elsewhere in East Africa. In Tanganyika rates vary, as between the Nyamwezi among whom it is high, and moreover where it increased from 1948 to 1957, and their immediate northern neighbours, the Sukuma, where the rate is low. This contrast between two adjacent tribes serves as an example of how a major difference may occur over a very short distance and it underlines the danger of generalizing from evidence that may be obtained from one particular tribe. Two main groups of factors – historical and geographical – have been responsible for the contrast between the Nyamwezi and the Sukuma. From at least the early decades of the nineteenth century the Nyamwezi

Table 6 Emigration rates

Tribe	Census	Males	Females	Both sexes
Tanganyika				
Nyamwezi	1948	15·0	9·4	12·1
	1957	17·5	12·7	15·0
Sukuma	1948	3·6	1·9	2·7
	1957	3·6	2·4	3·0
Chagga	1948	3·0	0·5	1·2
	1957	2·1	0·7	1·4
Haya	1948	5·7	1·9	3·2
	1957	3·8	2·6	3·2
Gogo	1948	4·7	2·0	3·3
	1957	7·9	3·7	5·7
Nyakyusa	1948	9·2	3·3	6·1
	1957	8·5	3·8	5·9
Makonde	1948	3·4	1·7	2·5
	1957	8·7	5·9	7·3
Makua	1948	7·4	3·6	5·5
	1957	11·4	4·8	8·1
Kenya	1948			
Kikuyu (*a*)		33·0	24·3	28·7
Luo		14·1	4·8	9·3
Kamba		12·9	6·2	9·4
Nyika (*a*)		0·7	0·9	0·8
Masai		11·5	9·1	10·3
Kikuyu (*b*)		25·4	21·9	23·6
Nyika (*b*)		3·7	2·9	3·3
Uganda	1948			
Ganda		6·3	5·3	5·8
Acholi		4·5	2·1	3·3
Ankole		19·2	9·9	14·4
Lugbara		17·7	6·9	12·2
Karamjong		1·4	0·8	1·1
Gisu		10·5	8·8	9·6
Kiga		3·8	1·4	2·5

Kikuyu (*a*) includes all those Kikuyu in Nairobi District, but even if these are excluded (*b*) the migration rate remains uniquely high. Nyika (*a*) are the figures for the whole tribe, (*b*) excludes those on Mombasa Island and treats them as migrants from their tribal lands.

Source: A. W. Southall, 'Population Movements in East Africa', in K. M. Barbour and R. M. Prothero (*ed.*), *Essays on African Population*, 1961.

lands were being crossed by main routes that led inland from the coast to Lake Tanganyika, along which passed Arab traders and slave-raiders and also the first European explorers. The Nyamwezi were made aware of other lands and other peoples from these contacts, which the Sukuma, with their lands away from main routes, did not experience. The Nyamwezi were thus provided with an incentive to migrate and were able to obtain information of those places to which they should migrate, where they were most likely to benefit economically. A long and well-established tradition of migration thus developed among them. The contrast between Nyamwezi and the Sukuma has been further emphasized by the better agricultural opportunities in Sukumaland for both cultivation and pastoralism, than in Nyamwezi country, which have given the Sukuma much less economic incentive to migrate in order to find work elsewhere. Among the Nyamwezi, where the opportunities for development in their home area are more restricted, the incentive to migrate is much greater. With them, therefore, both centrifugal and centripetal forces have operated to influence the development and persistence of labour migration. These forces have been observed in other parts of Africa.

The emigration rates for women were less than those for men among almost all the tribes assessed and in many instances they were less than half. This is a common feature throughout the continent, with the men going off in search of work and leaving their wives and families at home. The discrepancy between males and females is least among the tribes in East Africa with the highest overall rates of emigration; where the tradition of migration has been long established it is most likely that a comparable outward movement of women accompanying their menfolk will have developed. Though these different rates of migration between the sexes are not likely to affect the transmission of malaria, they do influence the incidence of other diseases, particularly the venereal diseases. Liaisons are common between male migrant labourers and prostitutes, during absences from home and from wives, with a resultant widespread incidence of gonorrhoea in particular. Furthermore, labourers transmit these veneral infections to their wives when they return home.

Labour migration in Tanganyika

Mobility associated with migrant labour is particularly notable in Tanganyika, both within the country and between it and adjacent countries. The movements of labour have developed since early in the present century and have taken place mainly to large-scale agricultural enterprises within Tanganyika and to mining and industrial concerns in the Rhodesias and in South Africa. Migrants are usually 'target' workers who set off with the intention of accumulating a particular sum of money, often for a special purpose, and they return to their home areas when they have earned this. Having once experienced such economic gain by working away from home, they frequently leave for further periods of employment. Thus there are continual comings and goings of migrant workers and the rate of labour turnover is considerable in the various forms of employment to which they go. It has been estimated that in Tanganyika as many as 300,000 persons are involved annually in movements, half of them going to work and the other half returning to their homes.

The single most important source of work for migrant labour in Tanganyika is the sisal-growing industry which employs about 130,000 workers. This industry has its own organization to recruit labour, but in fact this deals with only about thirty per cent of the total labour force. The majority of the labourers employed move to and from the sisal-growing areas making their own arrangements for travel and finding employment for themselves on the different estates. Movements to the estates and to other areas of economic development mean that migrants have to make journeys through, and into, parts of Tanganyika which are highly malarious and where the season of transmission of the disease lasts for six months of the year or more (Figure 16). Migrants coming from areas where malaria is less severe have little acquired tolerance and thus easily succumb to virulent infections. This happens especially with migrants coming from Rwanda and Burundi where the intensity of malaria infection is much reduced by the high altitude and the resultant climatic modifications which inhibit vector breeding. These migrants suffer physically, from illness and debility, and become more susceptible to other diseases, and economically through being incapable of work.

Efforts have been made by the government and by non-government agencies in Tanganyika to regulate the movements of migrant labourers within the country and across its boundaries, not only to alleviate hardship among them but also to protect the interests of the communities from which they originate and in which they work. This is an enormous task for it is difficult to implement satisfactory measures of control. Coincident with the need to establish regulation and control there has been the wish to increase the degree of stabilization in the labour force employed in Tanganyika. This is desirable from the points of view of both social welfare and public health. Many of the sisal estates have

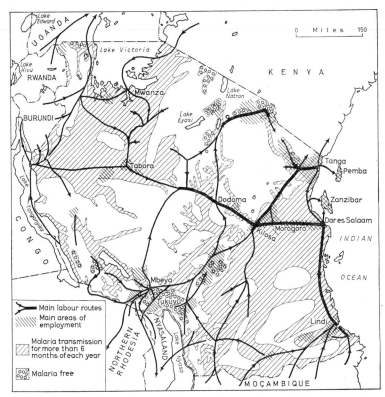

Figure 16 Movements of migrant labour in Tanganyika and adjacent countries, and the length of the malaria transmission season. (Based on maps by the author in *Bulletin, World Health Organization* and *Geographical Journal*.)

been contributing towards this end by improving amenities for labourers, and more particularly by providing facilities which enable them to be accompanied by their wives and children. Family accommodation, schools and medical services are now provided on the larger estates, often with standards which are above the average for Tanganyika. Towards the end of the 1950s there was some discernible decrease in the number of migrant labourers; now it remains to be seen whether this trend will continue with an independent government in Tanganyika.

Population stability and instability in Kenya

There is less information on labour migration in Kenya than for the other countries in East Africa, largely because the main movements take place within the country and they are considered to be of lesser importance than if adjacent countries were involved. This is the attitude that was presented officially when enquiries about labour movements were made in Nairobi some years ago. These internal movements are important for their effects on social and economic development and on public health. Migrants within the country are known to come mainly from Kikuyu, Embu and Meru in the Kenya Highlands (especially from the first of these), from Central Nyanza and from the coastal strip. They are attracted to urban areas with industrial development, to European farms in the Rift valley and to tea and sisal plantations in the highlands. These patterns of origin and destination developed during the first half of the present century, but they have been influenced and modified by events in Kenya during the last decade and are still in the process of changing at the present time.

During the Mau Mau emergency many of the Kikuyu squatter settlers on European farms, where they provided the labour force, were returned to their tribal reserves; subsequently with the return to peaceful conditions there was a reverse movement. Inside the Kikuyu reserves changes were also made during the emergency when the population was concentrated into villages from the traditional pattern of dispersed homesteads, so that more effective control could be exercised. Initially this change was unpopular, though largely because of the circumstances in which it was taking place. Subsequently its benefits have been recognized, particularly the much greater facility with which it is possible to make services such as dispensaries, schools and piped water supplies available.

For several years too the resettlement and redistribution of the rural population have been associated with schemes for consolidating land holdings in the reserves. These are meant to assist the development of sound agricultural practices, by ending insecurity of tenure and by doing away with the excessive fragmentation of land which had made many holdings uneconomic and incapable of providing more than bare subsistence. This process of consolidation has been applied discriminately, only where there has been a demand for it and where it was clear that the people fully understood what was happening. It has progressed furthest in Central and Nyanza Provinces. More recently, with the approach of independence, land that was formerly alienated to Europeans has been acquired and schemes have been initiated to settle African farmers on it. These will result in further movements and redistribution of population. The eventual effect of all this reorganization of land holdings and of settlements should be to lessen migrations, since farmers and their families will have the opportunity of making a more adequate living. Better amenities will be available and the population will be more favourably distributed for the promotion of mass campaigns to raise standards of health.

The improvements in economic and social conditions in the rural areas should also assist the official policy that has been directed towards the stabilization of the urban population of Kenya. The country's two major towns, Nairobi, the capital, and Mombasa, the main sea port, have attracted large numbers of people from the countryside and these have proved to be most unstable elements. From a survey of Africans in urban employment in the mid-1950s it was estimated that fifty per cent of the total of 350,000 were 'target' workers who tended to remain in employment for less than six months. Brief length of service characterized the employment of the majority of Africans in private industry in Nairobi.

Table 7 Length of service of African employees in private industry in Nairobi and Mombasa, 1954

	Number of years									
	under 1	2	3	4	5	6	7	8	9	over 10
	per cent									
Nairobi	48	20	12	6	3	3	2	1	1	3
Mombasa	40	17	12	8	6	4	2	1	1	7

Source: Report of a Committee on African Wages. Government Printer, Nairobi 1954.

Because of long-established control measures malaria is not a major problem in the urban areas of Kenya, but tuberculosis thrives in the overcrowded and often insanitary conditions in towns which have grown so rapidly in the last decade and a half that it has been impossible to provide adequate accommodation and services for their increased, but often transient, populations. In 1958–59 a survey to determine the incidence of this disease in Nairobi provided interesting evidence of the unstable character and rapid turnover of population. The survey was based on a ten per cent random sample, for which in the first instance various demographic data were collected. When medical examinations began only a week later, it was found that already there had been changes in the location of people in the sample. A year later it was possible to find only about a half of the original sample; of those who could not be traced it was estimated that approximately forty per

D

cent had left Nairobi while the remainder had moved elsewhere in the city. The difficulties of applying measures to improve public health to a population of this character, and the ways in which this instability must contribute to the transmission of disease, are too obvious to require elaboration. At the present time the problems of Kenya's urban population are magnified by an increase in unemployment due to the running-down of the country's economy, consequent on a lack of confidence with the coming of independence. This may be only temporary, but other basic problems associated with the rural exodus of population and the growth of towns remain. They are by no means unique to Kenya and are common throughout Africa.

Zanzibar and Pemba

The absence of effective barriers and of control points has been given as a reason which makes it impossible to insulate an area from movements of population that take place to and from it. In the case of the islands of Zanzibar and Pemba it might be reasonably assumed that there would be no problem of insulation, and that this would be complete in the literal and metaphorical senses of the term. However, this proves not to be the case. Each year there is an influx of potential human carriers of malaria into the islands which coincides with the time when the number of mosquito vectors is greatest. As a result, levels of malaria infection have remained high in spite of attempts to develop eradication with the use of insecticides and drugs. These carriers are labourers who come from the mainland of East Africa to help to pick the buds of the clove trees, and the islands supply about three-quarters of the world's production of cloves. The harvest lasts from July to January, with two main periods of picking, *mwaka* from July to September, and *vuli* from November to January.

Whether they come from the Tanganyika mainland adjacent to Zanzibar, or from farther afield, the migrant labourers either have come from or have passed through regions which are highly malarious. Some are reported as coming from as far away as Rwanda and Burundi and they acquire infections as they travel through Tanganyika. Zanzibar is one of the places to which the Nyamwezi have migrated and in each of the censuses from 1924 to 1957 between 6,000 and 8,000 of them have been recorded as a permanent element in the population. All the censuses have been taken out of the clove-picking season and so do not include the members of this tribe and of others who come each year for the harvest as temporary migrants.

If these temporary labourers are to be made innocuous as a reservoir of malaria infection knowledge is required of their numbers, of the ways by which they enter the islands, and of their movements within the islands. Estimates of the number of migrants vary from 15,000 to 50,000 and in any case it is probable that the total varies considerably from year to year with the size of the harvest and the wage being offered for picking cloves. Annual production in the past has ranged from 2,000 to about 40,000 tons, but recently there has been a glut on the world market and there is likely to be over-production for some time to come. The number of labourers coming from the mainland tends to fall when prices are low and it is possible that at these times most of the migrant pickers come to the islands by the recognized channels of entry. In the years when high prices prevail and the number of migrants increases, a proportion of them probably enters by ways that cannot be checked and controlled. There has, however, been no study made of these circumstances and these suppositions may be incorrect. But, whatever the circumstances of the clove harvest, it has been estimated that up to 8,000 labourers who are also malaria carriers, may come to the islands each year for other kinds of agricultural work.

The lack of any precise knowledge of the number of migrant labourers has been partly due to the absence of any close official check on people entering and leaving Zanzibar and Pemba. In the past there was no need for this, as any citizen of British East Africa was legally entitled to enter and leave the Zanzibar Protectorate. There were regular passenger sailings each week between Zanzibar and Dar es Salaam and twice-weekly between Zanzibar and Pemba by ships of H.H. the Sultan of Zanzibar. During the season of the clove harvest passages for labourers were free on the latter route and it had been suggested that the ending of these facilities would help to reduce the number of migrants. In addition to these sailings these routes were regularly served by other ships. In all these instances it would be possible to arrange a check on those in transit if this were necessary for the malaria eradication programme.

The problems arise from the unchecked entry of labourers about which very little is known, though probably most of these go to Pemba which produces about four-fifths of the clove crop. In 1960 immigration officers were of the opinion that the official figures gave correctly the movement of people in and out of Pemba, but they could scarcely be expected to express a contrary view. They argued that with free passages available there was no incentive for migrants to come and go other than by the normal routes. But this free transport was provided between Zanzibar and Pemba only and to take advantage of it, it was necessary first to make the crossing between the mainland and Zanzibar. People with long experience of Pemba state that there is almost continual movement backwards and forwards between the island and the mainland in small boats which carry up to twelve passengers. If conditions are favourable it is even possible to make the crossing by canoe. Movements of migrants by these means go completely unchecked and it would be impossible to check them, because of the nature of the Pemba coastline with its many inlets and bays in which to land, and the fact that the people who provide the transport are very competent sailors who would be capable of putting people ashore almost anywhere.

Apart from the movements of migrant labourers to and from Zanzibar and Pemba there are movements within the islands during the clove-picking season. Some of the owners of large numbers of clove trees recruit their labourers on the mainland, at Dar es Salaam or at Tanga, and these migrants presumably enter by the recognized routes and then remain with the one employer throughout the harvest. But two-thirds of the clove growers own less than fifty trees, and each would employ only a few pickers from the great reservoir of migrant labour that comes spontaneously to the islands. As is so often the case with labour migration in Africa there is a 'bush telegraph' system that operates between employer and labourer so that each knows where work and labour are available and when they are required. But the small employers keep no records of the labour they employ, so nothing precise is known of the movements of labourers when they reach the islands and of the ways in which they distribute themselves in order to find employment. It is said that a general movement of labourers takes place from south to north in Pemba as the harvest proceeds, but this does not appear to be regular. When there is a bumper harvest picking is taking place at the same time over the whole island, with resultant urgent and competing demands for labour. It has been suggested that official transit centres should be provided for migrant labourers at Wete and Chake Chake in Pemba, to facilitate their employment and to help to regulate movements. There is much to recommend this suggestion, for transit centres in Tanganyika have provided valuable data on labour migration and enable some degree of control to be exercised on migrants.

Clearly the information on the movements of migrant labourers to and from the islands of Zanzibar and Pemba is very conflicting and the data on them are very incomplete. Any reduction in the numbers of migrant labourers would assist the programme of malaria eradication which is now in the attack phase. However, even if transmission is interrupted successfully under these circumstances, the problem remains as to what will happen in the future when, with an improvement in the trade in cloves, there may be an increase in the number of migrant labourers who would provide a reservoir for possible reinfection. At the time of writing it is impossible to suggest what may happen in the immediate, let alone in the more distant future. Zanzibar's recent revolutionary change of government makes her political future and her economic future uncertain. Land on the islands has now been nationalized and the need to diversify the economy, by reducing dependence on cloves, has been emphasized. British East Africa is no more and migrant labourers into Zanzibar and Pemba are now the nationals of the independent states of Tanganyika, Uganda, Kenya, Rwanda and Burundi. It is conceivable that they may now be considered differently by the Zanzibaris, as compared with the past when all were under an alien colonial administration.

These imponderables apart, it has been maintained that labour for the clove harvest from within Zanzibar and Pemba is insufficient only in terms of the *present rate of production per picker* and that an increase in this rate would eliminate the need for migrant labour from the mainland. But whether the problems of labour migration will be solved in this way, or whatever may happen in the future as a result of political and economic changes, it is disturbing to find that for the malaria eradication programme in these islands it has not been possible to control the entry of sources of fresh infections. The fact that the malaria eradication programme in Zanzibar and Pemba has been concerned with only a very limited area, surrounded by sea which might be regarded as an effective barrier to movement, and yet has not been successful, serves to emphasize the magnitude of the problems that have to be dealt with on the African mainland.

The Kigezi pilot project in south-west Uganda

Natural barriers to movement, such as waterless or mountainous areas, have been used to some effect in the Middle East as the boundaries for malaria eradication schemes. In Africa, difficulty of access and therefore restriction on population movement may have been among the factors which contributed to the success reported in 1961 from the malaria eradication pilot project in the northern part of Kigezi District in south-west Uganda. The results achieved there have provided a

D2

glimmer of hope among the many difficulties that face malaria eradication in East Africa. Interruption in the transmission of malaria was achieved in one year, after two cycles of spraying with residual insecticides in some parts of the project area, and after three cycles plus a single-dose drug treatment in others where the malaria rates were higher.

The altitude of the project area ranges from about 3,000 feet to a little over 4,500 feet above sea-level, but this is insufficient to produce significant modifications in temperatures such as would affect mosquito breeding. However, steep slopes characterize the terrain and they limit the areas where water can collect and in which mosquitoes may breed. Human factors are also generally favourable. The location of all the population is well known for this is an area of resettlement, the Bachiga having been moved to it from the southern part of Kigezi District. There are about 50,000 people in the project area, at an average density of 300 persons per square mile which is high for rural areas in tropical Africa. Complete coverage was achieved in insecticide spraying, in spite of the fact that settlement is dispersed and not nucleated, though there were only permanent dwellings and no temporary shelters to deal with. Good residual effects were obtained with D.D.T. since the mud from which the walls of the huts were constructed had a low sorptive capacity. Though nearly all settlements had to be reached on foot none was more than five miles from a motorable road, and the existence of a reasonable network of roads greatly assisted the movement of spray teams and thus reduced the wear and tear on personnel and equipment. Contacts with the population were made easier, and their cooperation in the eradication measures was obtained by the fact that the Bachiga chiefs continue to wield considerably more authority than their counterparts in many other parts of Uganda.

On the basis of the experience in Kigezi it has been suggested that the interruption of malaria transmission should be attempted in central and western Uganda. While not minimizing in any way the success achieved in this project there is no doubt that factors of the physical environment and those relating to the people were more favourable in Kigezi than in many other malarious areas in tropical Africa. It is therefore probably over-optimistic to expect similar success under different circumstances in other parts of Uganda.

Migrant labour and malaria control in South-central Africa

Of the countries in the former Federation of Rhodesia and Nyasaland, Nyasaland was the main source of migrant labourers with the majority in the past going either to Southern Rhodesia or to South Africa. The other major source area was Moçambique. Migrant labourers have been employed in the two Rhodesias on large scale and well-organized enterprizes from which data are available. Some of the migrant labour is recruited but, provided that free movement of labour is allowed (it is not permitted to the Republic of South Africa), only a small proportion is dealt with by recruiting organizations. In the mid-1950s it was estimated that less than ten per cent of the migrant labour that had entered Southern Rhodesia since the war had been recruited. Where attempts have been made to curtail the movements of labour the restrictions have been circumvented and labourers have continued to go to work in the places which they have selected themselves. Altogether the patterns of intercountry migrations in this part of Africa are very complex, and as elsewhere in the continent national boundaries are not barriers to population movements. In contrast to West Africa and Zanzibar labour migration is not of a mass nature on a seasonal pattern; very large numbers of men are involved but there are continual comings and goings between home areas and places of work throughout the year.

The Copperbelt and Kariba

In Northern Rhodesia the Copperbelt is far and away the biggest employer of labour which originates both inside and from outside the country. Just over twenty-five per cent of those employed come from outside Northern Rhodesia, mainly from Nyasaland and Tanganyika, and the majority of labourers from within the country come from the Northern Province, with such smaller numbers from the Luapula valley, from the western parts of the country and from the Central and Eastern Provinces. Labour migration has continued despite the policy of the mining companies to encourage a stable and permanent labour force.

Malaria control is practised within the urban and mining areas of Northern Rhodesia and when cases of the disease are notified they are checked to discover the sources of the infection. In most instances the infection is shown to have been imported by migrants from the rural areas where there is no malaria control; yet in spite of the likelihood of infections being brought in from these sources no treatment to suppress them is given to labourers when they come to work in the mines for the first time, or when they return to them again after spending some time in their home villages. In contrast to this absence of treatment anti-malarial measures were taken with the 7,000 African workers who were employed at the peak period of work on the construction of the

Kariba dam on the Zambezi river, in addition to other forms of malaria control. When labourers first arrived at the site they were given drug treatment to cure existing infections and then regular chemoprophylaxis to protect them from further infections. To ensure this the protective drug was administered each week when labourers received their meat ration.

Between twelve and fifteen per cent of the labourers at Kariba were accompanied by their wives and children who were also supplied with prophylactic drugs. No attempt, however, was made to check whether the drugs supplied to this group were taken regularly but, since most of the malaria cases treated at Kariba were in fact among women and children, the evidence is that they were not. For the labour force the sickness rate, which included men who were being given treatment but who continued to work, was under three per cent, as compared with ten per cent in the labour force employed in the building of the Owen Falls dam in Uganda in the early 1950s. Unfortunately no follow-up studies were attempted of the Kariba labourers when the dam was completed and they dispersed to their home areas. These would have been difficult to organize but they might have provided some valuable information on what happened when the labourers were exposed again to malaria infection without the protection of the drugs which they had been receiving. It would be interesting to know if they had lost any of their acquired tolerance of malaria during the period when they were protected, and, if so, whether they were more readily and more seriously infected when the protection ceased.

Peripheral malaria control in Southern Rhodesia

For the last fifty years Southern Rhodesia has been a great area of attraction for migrant labourers coming from within and from outside the country to find employment in the mining and industrial areas or on the European farms. It has been estimated that between 120,000 and 130,000 migrants enter the country each year from Northern Rhodesia, Nyasaland and Moçambique. In these three countries there has been little or no attempt to control malaria and the migrant labourers coming from them have provided a constant source of malaria infection for Southern Rhodesia. Sample tests have shown that at least thirty-five per cent of the migrants are infected with malaria parasites. The main routes by which they enter Southern Rhodesia are known (Figure 17), and some attempt had been made at points on the boundaries where migrants can be checked to administer a single dose of an anti-malarial drug in an attempt to reduce infection. It should be possible to exercise

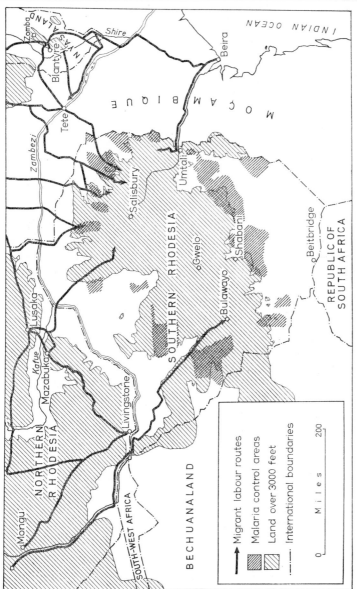

Figure 17 Movements of migrant labour into Southern Rhodesia and areas of malaria control. (Based on a map by the author in *Geographical Journal*.)

reasonably strict control over entry particularly where migrants from Northern Rhodesia and Nyasaland have to cross the Zambezi river.

The first large-scale scheme of malaria control in Southern Rhodesia was begun in 1949 in the Mazoe valley and there, as a result of spraying with residual insecticides, malaria infections were systematically reduced, particularly among the European population. In 1955–56 a peripheral barrier of areas subject to malaria control was established in an attempt to protect nearly the whole of the European population and a large proportion of the African population of Southern Rhodesia who live on the central plateau, the high veldt, at altitudes of between 4,000 and 5,000 feet (Figure 17). The high veldt tends to be invaded by mosquito vectors only during the wet season, from November to April, and there is no evidence of malaria transmission at other times of the year. By establishing the control areas in low-lying lands where the season of transmission is much longer and through which infected migrants pass, it was hoped to protect indirectly the much larger population on the high veldt. There were gaps in this peripheral barrier of control areas, in the north-west where the country is arid and the population is sparse, and in the north and south-west where there are European farms and ranches which employ only small numbers of African labourers. The exclusion of these European farming areas from control was based on the fact that Europeans will take adequate steps to protect themselves against malaria and therefore in Southern Rhodesia, as elsewhere in Africa, they are not an important factor in malaria transmission. The main reservoir of infection exists among the younger sectors of the African population particularly, and if infection can be prevented from spreading from them the most significant link in the chain of malaria transmission may be broken.

Political changes may influence the movements of migrant labour for with an independent government in Nyasaland an attempt may be made to reduce labour migration to Southern Rhodesia, whose European-controlled government and economic developments are viewed with disfavour. But the Nyasa migrant labourers make a significant contribution to the economy of their country with the money with which they return after working in Southern Rhodesia, and if this source of income were to end it would severely affect the Nyasaland economy. It is also very doubtful if the Nyasaland government could actually prevent labour migration to Southern Rhodesia continuing, even if it were to legislate against movements. What happens in the future will depend also on the measures that may be taken by the Southern Rhodesian government. In 1962 Southern Rhodesia concluded a new labour agreement with Moçambique which reduced the number of workers entering from that country to a quota fixed at 1,000 per month, a figure which is to be reduced subsequently. It is not possible to assess how well this agreement works in practice. Southern Rhodesia, however, has brought in regulations which require all those who enter the country to have a permit to work. Those who enter illegally have therefore the problem of finding work since they are unable to produce this document.

The political evolution, and revolution in the case of Zanzibar, in countries in East and South-central Africa has been so rapid in recent years and so unpredictable that it is impossible to forecast accurately the future effects of political change on migrant movements both within and between these countries. Some of the consequent changes have already been noted. A continuing hardening of attitude on the part of independent African states towards the Republic of South Africa is certain and further attempts will be made to lessen the flow of migrant labourers to the South African mines. If the present governments continue in Southern Rhodesia and in Angola and Moçambique then similar policies will be directed towards them. Within the newly independent states schemes for economic reorganization and development that are being planned and in some instances promoted (e.g. in Kenya and in Tanganyika), if they are successful, should reduce the economic incentive and in many instances the need for people to migrate in order to supplement their incomes. From the point of view of malaria eradication any reduction in labour migration will be desirable. But if large-scale schemes for eradication are to be planned in East and South-central Africa interterritorial cooperation will be as necessary for achieving success here as anywhere else in the continent; this may be difficult to obtain if relations continue to deteriorate between independent African states and those which remain controlled by European minorities. Political change may thus on the one hand work in favour of malaria eradication and on the other against it.

Brief reference to a new and recent type of population mobility in Africa may serve as an appropriate postscript to this chapter, for this also has been a direct result of political changes. Following the establishment in 1962 of an independent state in the former United Nations Trust Territory of Rwanda there have been outbreaks of violence between the Bahutu and the Watutsi – the majority and minority ethnic groups in the country. The former were traditionally the servile group under the overlordship of the latter and much of the recent trouble stems from attempts by some of the more extreme Watutsi to perpetuate this situation. Reprisals by the numerically superior Bahutu have led to some 120,000 Watutsi fleeing as refugees to the neighbouring countries of Uganda, Tanganyika, Burundi and the Congo. To all these countries, which are beset with many problems of their own, the refugees are an embarrassment and this is particularly so for Uganda which has the largest number. There have not been the resources immediately available to deal with the refugees and aid from other countries and from international bodies has been necessary.

Refugee movements similar to that from Rwanda have occurred in the last few years in the Congo, Cameroon, Togo and the Sudan particularly, but also in other parts of Africa. They too have been the result of instability consequent on political change. In a number of instances the instability has been the occasion for the recrudescence of traditional tribal rivalries which had been suppressed during the era of colonial rule. In the anarchic conditions in the Congo in 1960 an outbreak of tribal warfare between the Lulua and the Baluba led to the migration of 150,000 of the latter to the south of Kasai Province. Here, even when they were provided with land and seed, the Baluba were either too weak after their migration to cultivate or else arrived too late in the season to do so. Through lack of food and more particularly because of the absence of protein foods these people were subject to a severe epidemic of kwashiorkor, a deficiency disease. Besides dangers to health due to malnutrition and to the poor standards of shelter and the insanitary conditions in refugee camps, the movements of refugees may be a new factor that will have to be faced in the transmission of malaria and of other diseases, and a new element in mobility that will have to be taken into account when planning their eradication.

BIBLIOGRAPHY

General surveys of population mobility in East Africa and South-central Africa respectively are by A. W. Southall, 'Population Movements in East Africa', and by J. C. Mitchell, 'Wage Labour and Population Movements in Central Africa'; both are published in K. M. Barbour and R. M. Prothero (ed.), Essays on African Population, 1961. Studies relating to particular countries are A. I. Richards (ed.), Economic De-

velopment and Tribal Change, 1954 (for Uganda); H. R. G. Hurst 'A Survey of the Development of Facilities for Migrant Labour in Tanganyika during the period 1926–1959', *Bulletin, Inter-Africa Labour Institute* (Brazzaville), **6**, 1959, 50; J. C. Mitchell, 'The Distribution of African Labour by Area of Origin on the Coppermines of Northern Rhodesia', *Rhodes-Livingstone Journal*, **14**, 1954, 30; P. Scott, 'Migrant Labour in Southern Rhodesia', *Geographical Review*, **44**, 1954, 29, and 'The Role of Northern Rhodesia in African Labour Migration', *ibid.*, **44**, 1954, 432; J. R. V. Prescott, 'Migrant Labour in the Central African Federation', *ibid.*, **49**, 1959, 424. See also J. de Zulueta and others, 'The Result of the First Year of a Malaria Eradication Pilot Project in Northern Kigezi (Ugunda)', *East African Medical Journal*, **38**, 1961, 1, and W. Alves and D. M. Blair, 'Malaria Control in Southern Rhodesia', *Journal of Tropical Medicine and Hygiene*, **58**, 1955, 273.

7 West Africa

GREAT diversity of physical environments and of people characterizes West Africa, from Senegal in the west to Cameroon in the east. In a series of latitudinal zones vegetation types range from the dense luxuriant forest in areas of high rainfall adjacent to the Gulf of Guinea through the savanna and sahel to semi-desert on the arid margins of the Sahara in the north. From south to north the rainfall decreases, from 150 inches per annum and more to less than 20 inches, and the wet season becomes progressively shorter. North of latitude 12° N all but the largest rivers cease to flow in the dry season which lasts for more than six months. There is a general absence of surface water and supplies are limited even where underground sources have been exploited.

Despite these variations in moisture conditions, mosquito breeding in West Africa continues everywhere throughout the year and extends right up to the desert borders. Malaria is almost everywhere endemic and transmission is intense, though the levels of endemicity vary and they are lower in areas where the long dry season and the scarcity of water inhibit vector breeding. But in these areas a sharp rise in the number of mosquitoes follows the onset of the rains and there is a consequent rapid build-up in malaria transmission. Except in the higher parts of the Adamawa and Cameroon highlands in the east, at over 6,000 feet above sea-level, modifications of temperature by altitude are insufficient to affect mosquito breeding. There are no significant changes in the malaria situations on the Fouta Djallon plateau in Guinea or on the Jos Plateau in Nigeria, at altitudes of between 3,000 and 4,500 feet. Probably in no other part of Africa are there such extensive and continuous areas subject to malaria at high levels of intensity as are found in West Africa.

Faced with these enormous difficulties the projects for malaria control or eradication that have been organized in West Africa have been of a pilot nature, with the purpose of determining the nature and extent of the problems likely to be encountered if schemes on a larger scale were initiated. The pilot schemes have all involved only limited areas and relatively small numbers of people, and it is not surprising that they have been affected without exception by various types of population mobility, and that with other factors these have limited success and in some instances have been responsible for failure. The movements of Fulani pastoralists have influenced projects in the northern parts of

West Africa, where the physical environment makes seasonal movements of people and animals necessary but also eliminates or reduces the threat of trypanosomiasis to the herds of cattle. Pilgrims move eastward from West Africa towards Mecca, but as a factor in public health their influence in West Africa is much less than in the Republic of Sudan upon which they converge in large numbers. Localized seasonal movements of people associated with fishing and farming have prejudiced the progress of malaria projects in Liberia, Haute Volta and Togo. Movements of migrant labourers now probably involve the greatest numbers of people and their influence on efforts to control malaria in north-western Nigeria has already been indicated. In this chapter relationships between malaria and measures for its eradication, population movements and other geographical factors are illustrated by reference to certain pilot projects in West Africa.

Malaria control in western Sokoto

The malaria control project in the western part of Sokoto Province in north-western Nigeria was established in the first half of the 1950s with several interrelated aims. It was to test generally well-known principles of malaria control through the use of residual insecticide, adapting them to the specific local environmental and socio-economic conditions of a rural area in the savanna zone of West Africa. The methods employed were to be determined by experience, but they were intended to combine the maximum of economy in operation with the optimum results. These results were to be evaluated not only in terms of decreased sickness rates, effected both directly and indirectly by a reduction in the amount of malaria, but also in terms of the increased productivity which the area would experience from the general improvement in the health of its inhabitants. Estimates from inevitably incomplete data showed that the population was characterized by a high birth rate associated with high fertility, but this was accompanied by a mortality rate before puberty of over 500 per 1,000 live-births. The majority of these deaths was associated either directly or indirectly with intense malaria infection.

When the project began in April 1954 it covered an area of some 600 square miles containing a population of about 125,000. The area was divided into three zones and a different insecticide was used in each so that the relative effectiveness might be evaluated. In 1956 the project was expanded to cover 1,350 square miles and a population of 250,000, and was later extended to 7,000 square miles with a population of 500,000. It then covered parts of the Sokoto, Argungu and Gwandu

Divisions of Sokoto Province and so required the cooperation of three different Native Authorities when certain administrative decisions had to be taken. But during this time the two major problems encountered were not of an administrative nature, they were associated respectively with the main mosquito vector and with the human population.

Towards the end of 1955 the main vector, *A. gambiae*, was found to have developed a resistance to dieldrin, one of the insecticides in use and though it was not clear at the time this implied cross-resistance to another of the insecticides, B.H.C. D.D.T. was therefore substituted for each of these and was used throughout the whole project area and attempts were made to eradicate the focus of resistant *A. gambiae* by increasing the applications of insecticide.

The continued use of residual insecticide produced only a slow decline in malaria rates and it became evident that spraying would have to be supplemented with the use of drugs. These were administered successfully on a large scale and produced encouraging results. Though transmission was not interrupted, there was a marked decline in the rates of infection, especially among infants in whom infections were almost eliminated. Failure to achieve comparable results among the adult sections of the population could be attributed largely to human factors affecting the malaria situation – particularly the seasonal movements of Fulani pastoralists and of migrant labourers.

Some caution is needed in the use of the term Fulani in Northern Nigeria, and indeed throughout West Africa; for many centuries not all of the Fulani-speaking people have been nomadic pastoralists. In Sokoto five groups of Fulani have been distinguished and they differ from one another to a very large extent in the degree of settled and fixed living that each has attained. Thus, the *Torobbe* are a small aristocratic group who gave up nomadic ways many generations ago. From this group have come the ruling emirs and more recently many of the members of the governments of the Northern Region and of the Federation of Nigeria. Also completely settled is the large group of *Fulanin Zaure* who live, as their name indicates, in towns. The semi-settled Fulani cultivate crops and herd cattle, having permanent dwellings in towns and villages which are always occupied by the heads and older members of families. The younger members in this group move with the cattle, particularly during the wet season when pastures must be found away from the lands which are under cultivation, so as to prevent damage by animals to growing crops. This group is more settled than the semi-nomadic Fulani who combine some cultivation with their pastoral activities, but seldom have permanent homes to which they return. All the members in this group move with the herds when they are taken to a new grazing area and the herds are always kept together, except possibly at the time of year when the cattle tax (*jangali*) is being collected and attempts are made to escape payment. The Fulani in this group cultivate only *gero*, a fast-maturing millet which requires them to remain near the lands under cultivation for only a relatively short time. The *Borororo* are completely nomadic Fulani who never farm and whose lives and movements are entirely governed by the needs of their animals for pasture and water. They are found only in areas where there are few cultivators or none at all. With the semi-nomadic Fulani they are classed as *Fulanin daji*, 'bush Fulani', and in the 1952 census they represented under twenty per cent of the total number of Fulani in Sokoto Province, though in all the divisions except Sokoto their proportion was much higher.

Table 8 Fulani in Sokoto Province (1952 census)

Division	Total Fulani population	Fulanin daji
Sokoto	316,972	36,894
Gwandu	57,889	21,819
Argungu	16,757	9,569
Yauri	4,683	4,000
Sokoto Province	396,301	72,282

Figure 18 shows the general directions followed by a representative number of Fulani groups in the course of their annual migrations; the actual routes that are followed are much more complex. They move northward during the wet season and southward in the dry, an average distance of seventy-three miles in each direction, seeking water and pasture for their cattle. When questioned, the Fulani say that they are accustomed to migrate and so continue to do so. With the growth of population in recent years there have been increases in the amounts of land under cultivation and these restrict the movements of pastoralists. Conflicts between them and cultivators are common, through damage to crops by the one and the cultivation of traditional grazing lands by the other.

There are no truly nomadic Fulani in the project area and it is the semi-nomadic element which is the menace. Although they number only about 18,000, representing a little under four per cent of the population in the project area, their effect on attempts to establish malaria control has been considerable. Because of their seasonal movements they are difficult to locate for spraying and for drug treatment, and the duration of the residual effects of insecticide is limited on the grass huts in which they live. Surveys carried out after the completion of a cycle of spraying have shown that up to forty per cent of Fulani dwellings remained un-

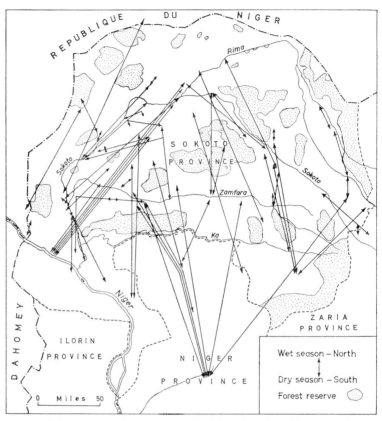

Figure 18 Movements of Fulani groups in Sokoto Province, Northern Nigeria. (Based on a map by the author in *Geographical Journal*.)

treated, either because they had been missed out or because they had been erected after the spraying had taken place. As a result mosquito densities have been found to be consistently higher in the Fulani camps than in the permanent villages and the spleen and parasite rates among the Fulani were scarcely affected by the measures that had been applied.

In an attempt to meet these problems a separate group was established in the project team in 1959 to spray the camps of the Fulani and to distribute a single curative dose of drug to them. The operations of this group showed that the number of Fulani huts that could be sprayed per man per day was only one-third the rate for permanent dwellings and that, because of their scattered distribution, on average one mile of transport had to be run for each hut that was sprayed. These requirements are obviously very expensive in time, manpower and money. Furthermore, even when the camps have been located, there are difficulties in making a successful approach to the Fulani who are reserved and resent the inevitable intrusion and interferences that malaria eradication measures involve. Frequent visits, during which general medical treatment is given, are needed in order to gain their confidence and to get them to cooperate.

In Northern Nigeria there is as yet no official policy for deciding the future of the nomadic Fulani, though various suggestions have been made of possible ways of changing their way of life. There is evidence that for some of them this is happening spontaneously. The semi-settled Fulani would probably settle permanently if adequate pasture and water could be made available for their cattle. They say that if their cattle could be 'made at home' then they themselves would settle down. The settling of nomadic or semi-nomadic Fulani by official or unofficial means will be a slow business and is not likely to be accomplished in such time as to affect significantly programmes for malaria eradication. They have therefore to be accepted as an unstable element in the population, and in the event of large-scale schemes for malaria being organized in the northern parts of West Africa provision will need to be made for special attention to be given to them. One thing that is vital is to recognize the variations that exist within this major ethnic group and thus not fall into the error of considering all the Fulani in one category requiring one method of treatment.

When the Sokoto project was started it was known that there were movements of people from the area in October and November, at the beginning of each dry season, and that they returned in April for the beginning of the next wet season. It was estimated at the time that up to ten per cent of the population might be involved in these movements and this proved to be a serious underestimate. There had been a census of migrant labour carried out in Sokoto Province in the dry season of 1952–53 by the Nigerian Department of Statistics; it had shown that from some districts, particularly in the northern parts of the province, between twenty-five and fifty per cent of the adult males in the population might be away from home during each dry season. To a very large extent these are the *yan tuma da gora* ('the young men who travel with a gourd') who travel great distances to find work elsewhere in Northern

Nigeria, in the southern parts of the country and in Ghana. Seasonal migrants in this group would comprise some of the unstable element in the population of the malaria project area, though the numbers away are probably not as high a proportion as in the north of the Province. In addition there are the *masu cin rani*, who move over much shorter distances in the dry season each year, but whose journeys often extend beyond the boundaries of the project area. These are people of all ages and of both sexes and often whole families are involved.

The *yan tuma da gora*, who travel great distances, inevitably pass through and live in highly malarious areas and return from them with infections which help to maintain the reservoir of malaria transmission. People travelling only limited distances are also likely to become infected if they go outside the project area, and, in fact, the children in this group are particularly susceptible. Sample surveys have shown that malaria infection rates in these migrant groups are about double those in the settled population.

Although it has proved impossible to interrupt malaria transmission among the population in the project area in western Sokoto, the success achieved in lowering malaria rates, particularly among the more settled elements in the population, has been encouraging. Failure to end transmission has been experienced also in other pilot projects in the savanna zone of West Africa, in the north of Cameroon and in Haute Volta. In these schemes too the use of residual insecticides was complemented by the large-scale distribution of drugs. Failures have been due in part to the development of resistance to insecticides by the main vector (*A. gambiae*) and to various human factors which are similar to those in Sokoto. The most important has been the failure to achieve complete coverage in insecticide spraying, which again has been largely due to the presence of various mobile elements in the population. Another difficulty has arisen from the fact that a sizeable proportion of the population may be in the habit of sleeping out-of-doors at certain times of the year, and at these times they may be bitten by infected mosquitoes with exophilic habits. These mosquitoes are not affected by the residual insecticides sprayed on the insides of buildings since they never come into contact with them. Difficulties which arise from sleeping outside are less, however, if this habit is restricted to the hot season of the year only when the numbers of vectors are reduced by aridity.

Northern Ghana: the use of medicated salt

One attempt to solve the problem of regularly administering antimalarial drugs to large numbers of people has been by the distribution of medicated salt (common salt to which an anti-malarial drug has been added) for domestic consumption. The Pinotti method, named after its originator, was first used in Brazil in 1959–61 when it was applied on a large scale in the Amazon valley. Factors there seemed to be particularly favourable for a trial since all the salt imported into the area was used only for domestic purposes and its distribution was in the hands of only a limited number of agents. Effective control of the sources of supply and of the organization for distributing salt is obviously necessary. In spite of these relatively favourable conditions in Brazil the effect on malaria of drugs administered in this way was so limited that the experiment there was not continued.

However, it is still believed that this method may be of use, and two pilot projects for the distribution of medicated salt have been established in Africa, one in Tanganyika and the other in northern Ghana. The latter is located in the central part of northern Mamprusi, in the north-east corner of Ghana, in an area covering 400 square miles with an estimated population of 60,000. Here the initial work in establishing the project was concerned with determining the sources of the salt in the area and the organization of retail distribution since these were not known. It is obviously easier to treat and to distribute refined salt, but salt from local sources to which people are accustomed may be all that they are prepared to use. A major factor, therefore, that might well prejudice the extended use of this method in many of the northern parts of West Africa, is that much of the salt used still comes from the traditional sources of supply in the Sahara desert. These are the oases of Taoudeni and Bilma in the western and eastern Sahara respectively.

Salt was one of the major products of Saharan trade in the past, and from time immemorial great camel caravans have come from these two oases each year to distribute salt to the inhabitants of the Western Sudan. At the beginning of this century the *azalai*, the salt caravan which annually made the hazardous three-week journey from Agades to Bilma for supplies, still consisted of some 20,000 camels. Numbers are now much less, but still in the months of January and February groups of from 75 to 100 camels from the main caravan may be encountered moving southward from Niger, taking Bilma salt into Northern Nigeria. In many of the villages and towns of Northern Nigeria the Bilma product far exceeds the amount of imported salt that is for sale. It is brought from Bilma in the form of pillars, about four to five feet in length and six inches in diameter; for retailing, these are divided into pieces of varying size and price. The salt is hard and crude, grey or dirty fawn in colour and in complete contrast in texture and colour to the refined salt which is imported from Europe. Nevertheless it is the traditional product which is the one that is preferred, and attempts by trading firms to popularize imported salt have met with only very limited response from people who are basically conservative in their habits and tastes. To control the source and distribution of Bilma salt would be a difficult if not impossible task and, furthermore, its hardness and the fact that it is not crushed before sale would make the introduction of an anti-malarial drug impossible.

In its early stages the Ghana pilot project was particularly successful and spectacular declines in parasite rates, from eighty to five per cent, were observed within a few months. Subsequent difficulties arose as a result of a reduction in the use of medicated salt and a reversion to the use of untreated salt. This change was found to be due to people having realized the efficacy of the medicated salt and so deciding to keep it for use only when they were ill. In ceasing to use it regularly they failed to maintain an adequate intake of the drug which would give them protection against malaria. It is unlikely that the Pinotti method of administering antimalarial drugs would be capable by itself of interrupting the transmission of malaria, particularly in areas where there is high endemicity. Apart from many problems which are likely to be encountered in organizing the distribution of medicated salt there are other disadvantages in its use. It is obviously very difficult to control the amount of a drug that is taken in this way. Investigations have shown that breast-fed infants and young children usually receive either very little or no salt, and thus persons in the age-groups which most require treatment and protection against malaria are likely to go either insufficiently treated or untreated. Total coverage of the population is thus not complete. It may be possible to use medicated salt most effectively in association with other anti-malarial measures, though there are some circumstances where factors relating to the human population or to the vector may make it the only method that can be used. This could be so in areas where there is a settled population that is widely dispersed at a low density, or with nomadic peoples. In either case it would be very expensive and difficult to achieve total coverage with insecticide spraying. Salt might also be used where dwellings are unsuitable for the effective application of residual insecticides and the maintenance of their toxic effects, or where the main mosquito vector is exophilic, and by resting out-of-doors would not be affected by spraying with residual insecticides.

The Kpain project, Liberia

In contrast to the unsuccessful attempts to interrupt malaria transmission in the pilot projects in the savanna zone of West Africa some measure of success has been achieved in two projects located in the forest zone – one in central Liberia centred on Kpain, the other in the Yaoundé area of Cameroon. The Liberian project, when it was originally established in 1953, was intended to test the effectiveness of spraying with residual insecticides in an area with high malaria endemicity, where transmission lasted throughout the year and reached peaks in July/August and November/December. In the area that was first treated the population numbered 54,000, but the zone of operations was subsequently extended to cover 300,000 people.

Problems presented by the physical environment were particularly difficult. The terrain of alternating ridges and valleys provided ideal breeding places for vectors on the swampy floors of the latter, while the thick forest cover made access difficult to all parts of the project area and some parts were impenetrable. Dwellings were not only remote but were also widely dispersed, and nearly ninety per cent of them could be reached by spray teams only on foot. In addition to these difficulties various habits and customs of the population prejudiced the success of operations. Sleeping out-of-doors was common, and frequent replastering of the inside walls of dwellings nullified the intended effects of insecticide. A large proportion of the population spent the main season of agricultural activity living in temporary shelters on their farms, and these shelters could not be included in the normal cycle of spraying since they were erected after it had taken place. By occupying these shelters for several months of each year people were without protection for the period when malaria transmission is most intense. To add to all these difficulties the main vector (*A. gambiae*) developed a resistance to dieldrin with a consequent need to change the residual insecticide. In the face of all these setbacks it is not surprising that the initial attempt to interrupt malaria transmission in the Kpain project was unsuccessful. Many important lessons were learnt, though only at the expense of very great hardship for those engaged in the work.

On the basis of this experience the project was reorganized. In the first instance, before applying any further eradication measures, more information was accumulated on malaria, mosquitoes and human beings in the project area. More intensive surveys of the distribution of settlements revealed that about forty per cent of the houses had been missed out in the previous operations and that the interior surfaces of the high roofs, which are a feature of the houses, had either gone unsprayed or else had been inadequately treated. From these investigations it was found that a much greater surface area in dwellings needed to be sprayed than had previously been calculated. Particular attention was paid to health education, to make people aware of the work in progress and to explain the measures being undertaken, so that a greater degree of cooperation was obtained than formerly. On the basis of this essential preliminary work a new programme of spraying with D.D.T. was planned and carried out which succeeded in interrupting the transmission of malaria. This has been a recent success and it remains to be seen whether interruption can be maintained for a sufficiently long time to achieve malaria eradication.

The results obtained in the pilot projects in the forest zone of West Africa provide more hope for malaria eradication than those in the savanna areas, and overall for this region it is possible to indicate some of the advantages and disadvantages for future progress. Over much of West Africa levels of endemicity are high, and the season of transmission is long and often without any break. There have been more instances of the development of resistance by the vector to insecticides in this part of the continent than elsewhere. In proportion to its area there are a greater number of independent states in West Africa than in any other major region of the continent. This territorial fragmentation inevitably increases the problems of developing interterritorial cooperation and coordination for malaria eradication, and between a number of the countries relations have not been always cordial since they became independent. Furthermore, their respective colonial backgrounds add to the difficulties of contact through language differences. The need to recognize these differences was illustrated when the World Health Organization recently established malaria eradication training schools at Lomé in Togo and Lagos in Nigeria, for personnel from French-speaking and English-speaking countries respectively.

In spite of political problems a start has been made to establish an interterritorial eradication project to include Cameroon, Nigeria, Dahomey and Togo, and ideally this should be extended to cover a much larger area of West Africa (see page 133). Levels of social and economic development among the various West African countries place them in a relatively advantageous position to pursue measures for malaria eradication, but even those that are best-off will require assistance in personnel and materials to mount large-scale schemes. But by comparison with the Sudan, countries like Nigeria, Ghana and Ivory

Coast should be in a position to do more than they are at present. Not only are their present economic positions good by African standards, but it can be argued that economic development would be advanced appreciably if there were overall improvement in the health and, thereby, the efficiency of their inhabitants such as would come with reductions in malaria. If these improvements were effected they would undoubtedly lead to increases in population with the reduction of mortality rates in the younger age-groups. The full implications of such demographic changes have not yet been realized anywhere in the world; undoubtedly they would be very considerable for a country with high levels of endemic malaria in which successful eradication took place.

BIBLIOGRAPHY

R. J. Harrison Church, *West Africa: A Study of the Environment and of Man's Use of it*, 1963, is a major source of information on the geography of this part of the continent. Relevant recent studies of the Fulani are: C. Hopen, *The Pastoral Fulbe Family in Gwandu*, 1958; Marguerite Dupire, *Peuls Nomades*, Paris, 1962; C. J. Hanson-Smith, *Notes on the Sokoto Fulbe*, 1955 (unpublished), and D. J. Stenning, *Savannah Nomads*, 1959. The authority on migrant movements in Ivory Coast and Ghana is J. Rouch, author of 'Migrations au Ghana', *Journal de Societé des Africanistes*, **24**, 1956, and director of a major survey of migration in the two countries in 1958–59, under the auspices of the Commission for Technical Co-operation in Africa South of the Sahara. The results of this survey have not yet been published, but there is a brief report in *Africa*, **29**, 1959, 417. Various papers by the author have been given in the bibliographies to earlier chapters.

E

8 Morocco

BECAUSE of its position north of the Sahara the problems of migrants and malaria in Morocco provide interesting comparisons and some contrasts with those to the south of the desert in the tropical parts of the continent. The malaria situation at the present day has still to be investigated in detail, though after nearly half a century of control measures applied by the French the disease probably remains only in residual areas. For this reason and because of factors of the physical environment it does not affect the country to the same extent and degree of intensity, and for the whole or greater part of the year, as in much of tropical Africa. However, the intention is to eliminate malaria entirely from Morocco and a project for malaria eradication is in the process of being developed.

General geographical factors

Within the country there are great variations in altitude and relief and in the higher parts of the Atlas and Rif mountain ranges, at over 5,000 feet above sea-level, the temperatures which prevail for many months of the year are too low for mosquito-breeding (Figure 19). There is great variety in the amounts of rainfall, with considerable influence exercised by relief upon the pattern of distribution; in the south and east of Morocco towards the northern borders of the Sahara desert the average annual rainfall is less than eight inches and the areas in which vectors can breed are severely restricted in extent. However, even here mosquitoes are found in the scattered oases where there is permanent water, and the sedentary inhabitants of these suffer from malaria.

Contrasts in human circumstances are to be found in variations in the distribution and density of the population and in its rural and urban character, in forms of settlements and in types of dwellings, in occupations and in social organization. Many of these human elements are influenced by physical factors and together they produce striking regional contrasts within Morocco's boundaries, though these enclose one of the smaller countries in Africa (174,000 square miles).

Morocco's population of more than 11,000,000 is concentrated in those parts of the country with relatively higher rainfall and better water supplies, which lie to the north and west of a line from Goulimime in the south-west to the lower Moulouya valley and thence to Oujda in the north-east (Figure 20). Nine-tenths of the population is located in

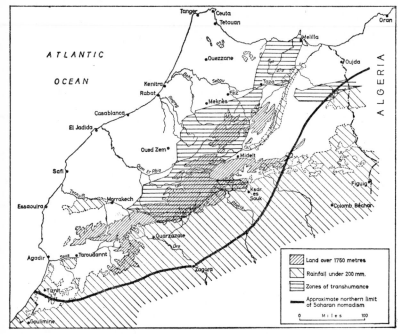

Figure 19 Morocco: physical factors, zones of transhumance, the limit of Saharan nomadism. (Based in part on maps in *Atlas du Maroc*, Rabat.)

less than half of the total area, with only ten per cent in the Atlas mountain ranges and the desert borders of the south and east. Particularly dense concentrations occur, for example, in the Sebou valley, in the piedmont zone of the High and Middle Atlas, on the high plains of Mèknes and Fès, and in the Pays de Doukkala. These concentrations have been influenced in the past by movements of population, but in their effect on the pattern of population distribution the outstanding movements have been from the interior of the country to the Atlantic coast. More than twenty per cent of the population of Morocco is now concentrated in a narrow coastal zone about 30 miles wide, extending for less than a hundred miles between the towns of Casablanca and Kenitra, and including the capital, Rabat, with its twin town Salé.

Regional variations in settlement patterns and house types are in part related to the distribution of the population, but are also influenced by physical factors and by ethnic differences. Dispersed settlement is characteristic on much of the plains and plateaux which lie between the Atlantic coast and the Atlas ranges. Such a settlement pattern will complicate a malaria eradication programme by increasing the distances

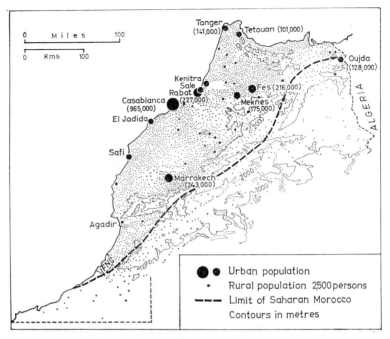

Figure 20 The distribution of population in Morocco, 1960. (Based on a map in D. Noin, *L'Information Géographique*, **26**, 1962.)

that have to be travelled in spraying operations and by increasing the likelihood of failure to obtain a complete coverage in the treatment of dwellings. Nucleated settlements may also present particular problems. In the large multiple-roomed *ksour* in the south and east of the country, which were built for protection and are in a sense both dwellings and settlements, it will be difficult to ensure complete coverage with insecticide of the multiplicity of surfaces and the great areas to be sprayed.

Data are being collected on the distribution of different types of dwellings and on the materials used in their construction, since these influence the effectiveness of residual insecticides. Continuing analysis and revision of these data will be essential, particularly in those parts of Morocco where several types of dwelling occur together in the same settlement. On the coastal plain between Rabat and Casablanca the dwellings in a village may consist of *khaima* (tents), *nouala* (beehive-shaped huts constructed of thatch on a framework of poles) and *maison de pisé* (square or rectangular houses with mud walls and a flat mud roof). A combination of such different types of dwellings indicates a trend towards more settled ways of living with the general adoption of more permanent dwellings which are represented by the *maison de pisé*, and the materials from which this is constructed retain the toxic effects of insecticide more efficiently than those of the *nouala* and *khaima*.

Population mobility

There are important elements in Morocco's population which are mobile – nomads and semi-nomads, pastoralists practising trans-humance, migrant labourers and those who are moving from the country-side to the towns. Each of these groups has its particular characteristics, many of which are relevant for malaria eradication. Within each group there are variations, and all of these groups are in the process of evolu-tion. Movements of cultivators to temporary dwellings on farms do not occur in Morocco. The majority of Moroccans are Muslims and many make the pilgrimage to Mecca, but the pilgrim movements are organized and controlled, and therefore do not have to be reckoned as a factor affecting malaria eradication.

Pastoral nomads

These people follow their traditional ways of life in the southern and eastern peripheral parts of the country, where the malaria situation has still to be evaluated, so that it is not yet known whether they play any significant part in it. The medical authorities at Agadir strongly main-tained that there was no malaria among the nomads in their province and the southern limit of insecticide spraying proposed for 1962 accepted this as a fact (Figure 21). But it is known that there is malaria in the oases that line the valleys which run southward from the Anti-Atlas, High Atlas and Jebel Sahro. The sedentary populations of these oases are infected and contacts between them and nomads are likely to result in malaria transmission.

The nomads still maintain some elements of their traditional overlord-ship and protection of these settled oases communities, and they come regularly each year at the time of the date harvest to receive a portion of the crop. Other more frequent, but less regular, contacts between nomads and the settled groups occur at the markets (*souk*). The nomads come to the *souk* particularly to buy tea and sugar, but in these contacts generally only the men of the nomad groups are involved. Nomad encampments are always located at some distance from the towns and villages where the *souk* is being held, and this siting seems to be quite deliberate. Not only are the nomads reserved and prefer to be apart, but by doing so the risk is diminished of contracting various diseases

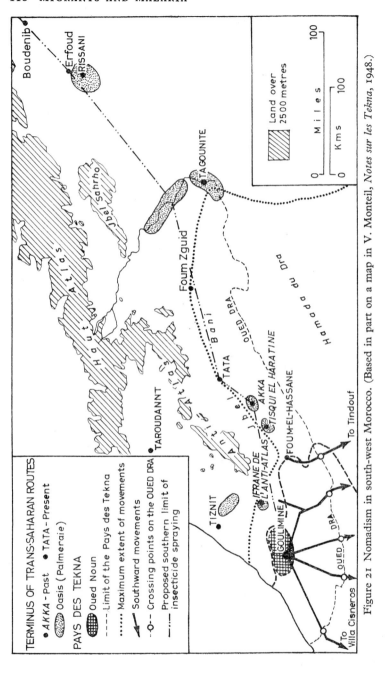

Figure 21 Nomadism in south-west Morocco. (Based in part on a map in V. Monteil, *Notes sur les Tekna*, 1948.)

which flourish among the settled communities. At Goulimime in the south of Agadir Province, where the most important camel market on the north-western borders of the Sahara is held, nomad camps ring the town at distances of between one and one and a half miles. Only the men attend the camel market and the *souk* and the women, children and old people remain in the camps. At the end of the day the men return to the camps and are thus not in the permanent settlements at night when vector activity is greatest and when there is most risk of acquiring malaria infections.

If nomads are found to be infected with malaria it will be essential to establish regular contacts with them in order to spray their tents and to administer anti-malarial drugs. This will prove immensely difficult with people whose life takes them great distances over some of the most difficult terrain, and in some of the worst climatic conditions, in the world. The Tekna, a nomadic tribe in south-western Morocco, exemplify the range of nomadic movements (Figure 21) and also the variety that may be found in one group. The core of the Pays des Tekna is the Oued Noun and here important annual fairs are held at Asrir, Ksabi and Goulimime. Though they are ethnically homogeneous the Tekna are divided into a number of distinct sub-groups whose ways of life differ from one another. The camel nomads range far southward into the Sahara and have interests in the oases as 'protectors' of their sedentary populations. Pastoral nomads of the sahel (the desert borders) have some minor interests in cultivation and in trade, though these are greater among the semi-nomads in the Oued Noun. Lastly there are some of the Tekna who have abandoned nomadic pastoralism altogether to become sedentary cultivators in the south-western foothills of the Anti-Atlas. Such variety within one tribe would be significant in planning a malaria eradication programme; each of these groups would present different problems and would require different consideration and treatment.

The camel nomads travel farthest afield, and some of the movements of this group may extend as far as Villa Cisneros in Spanish Sahara, to Tindouf and even southward to the valley of the Senegal river which forms the boundary between Mauretania and Senegal (Figure 21). On their journeys to and from the south, the Tekna cross the valley of the Oued Dra at recognized places which might be used for making contact for spraying and for drug distribution. When they are farther south in the great wastes of the western Sahara it would be very difficult to maintain any sort of contact with them. It has been suggested that some nomads could be trained in elementary hygiene and public health measures to assist with malaria eradication among their fellows; but it is unlikely that many would be found with even the minimum amount of education that would be necessary. Even if some were trained, there is still the problem that the camel nomads move only in small groups, because of the limited amounts of pasture and water that are available, and each tribal *aide* would thus be able to maintain contact with only a small number of people.

A further possibility for making contacts with nomads is at a *rassemblement* ordered by the administration, though this method is unlikely to prove very satisfactory. Administrative officers always claim to be able to bring everyone together in such an assembly when one is announced, though they could hardly be expected to admit that anything less than this would happen. A system for establishing contacts with the nomads at the *souks* might be organized in Morocco. For each province there is a *Calendrier des Souks et des Moussems* which gives in detail the locations and times of all markets and fairs, together with data on the produce in which they deal. Using this information programmes might be worked out for malaria eradication teams to visit all *souks*, and to administer drugs to all those who attend, the sedentary as well as the nomadic elements in the population.

The problems associated with nomadic people in the south of the country are further complicated by the absence of acknowledged and defined boundaries between Morocco and adjacent Spanish territories, Algeria and Mauretania. Like all the newly independent African states Morocco abhors the continuation of Spanish colonial rule in Africa and she claims Mauretania as her territory by historic right. Friction with Algeria over boundary problems in the latter part of 1963 developed into major incidents in which the armed forces of both countries were involved. Nomads move across these ill-defined and disputed frontier zones, and in the case of the Beni Guil across the defined boundary between Morocco and Algeria which runs from the Mediterranean Sea southward to Figuig and thence westward to the vicinity of Colomb Béchar. Where such interterritorial nomadic movements take place little can be achieved, either in malaria eradication or in the control of other diseases, without full cooperation and coordination between Morocco and Algeria.

While some countries have adopted specific policies for the nomads in their populations there is no such policy for them in Morocco. Nomads were not mentioned in the *Plan Quinquennial* for development between 1960 and 1964, and presumably, since they are such a small proportion (under five per cent) of the total population, it is assumed that they can virtually be ignored. Though they are small in numbers and unimportant in their influence on the Moroccan economy, like the Fulani in West Africa they may still be a major menace to public health. The absence of any definite policy for them only increases the difficulty of making useful practical suggestions for dealing with them in a malaria eradication programme. It is not easy to plan for people whose existence is barely acknowledged and some of whom anyhow spend large parts of each year outside recognized Moroccan territory.

Transhumance

Transhumance flourishes in the mountainous lands and the movements of those who practise it are related closely to the need to find pasture and water (Figure 19). Movements are mainly in vertical directions, and compared with nomadism they are more clearly defined and more rigidly adhered to, both in space and in time.

In Morocco the most important region of transhumance is in the mountains of the Middle Atlas, though it is also practised in the central parts of the High Atlas and to a lesser extent in the eastern Rif mountains. During summer transhumance, from May to October, the flocks and herds are moved away from the heat and aridity of the lower-lying valley floors to the higher pastures from which the snow has melted and where the grazing is good (Figure 22). As summer advances even some of these pastures become parched and arid and for this reason the animals have to be moved downward again, even before the falling temperatures and the first snow-falls herald the onset of the next winter. Winter transhumance, from November to March, involves movements away from the mountains to the adjacent lower-lying plateaux. Some groups, like the Beni Mguild in the Middle Atlas, practise double transhumance, moving upwards in summer and downwards in winter (Figure 23). Others move only in summer and spend the winter in their permanent villages.

The great volume of traditional transhumant movements began to diminish during the 1930s when the French pacification of Morocco was completed and former ways of life consequently began to change. A recent study of transhumance in Morocco, carried out in the upper Moulouya valley in the Middle Atlas, has indicated that a certain amount of official administrative control is now being exercised over movements, regulating the routes that are followed and the pastures that are grazed. These measures are directed towards improving conditions for the people and their animals, and the aim is to develop more intensive forms of pastoralism with consequent raising of the standards

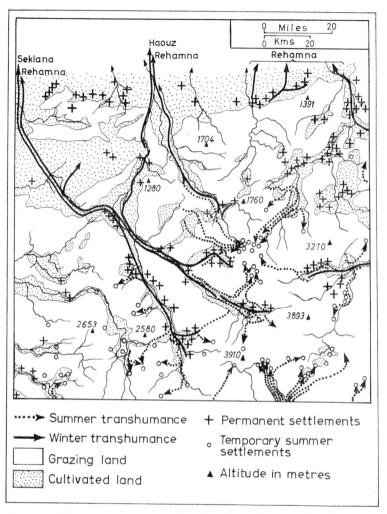

Figure 22 Transhumance in part of the High Atlas, Morocco. (Based on a map in J. Dresch, *Documents sur les Genres de Vie de Montagne dans le Massif Central du Grand Atlas*, 1941.)

of living. The attitudes of the pastoralists to these measures are typical of those of their fellows in other parts of Africa and elsewhere in the world. They are largely apathetic, more concerned with the number of animals that they own than with their condition, and they show little interest in the improvements which it is hoped will be effected.

It is among people with such conservative and unenthusiastic atti-

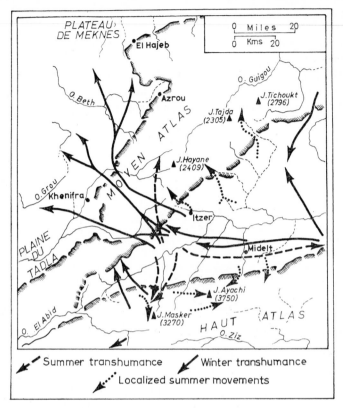

Figure 23 Transhumance in the upper Moulouya valley in the Middle Atlas, Morocco. (Based on a map in R. Raynal, *La Terre et l'Homme en Haute Moulouya*, Rabat, 1960.)

tudes to new ideas that malaria eradication measures will have to be applied. To do so successfully will require educating people to understand why they are necessary and why their cooperation is essential. Some medical authorities in Morocco are sceptical of being able to obtain people's acceptance of measures and to gain their cooperation. These are likely to prove more difficult than the problems of arranging an eradication programme to accommodate transhumant movements. The elements of regularity in the movements should make it possible to time measures to ensure adequate coverage in either spraying or in drug distributions. Distances traversed in transhumance, which extend up to a maximum of seventy miles, are much less than those covered by nomads.

Labour migration

Labour migration is a much less important element in the general population mobility in Morocco than it is in many parts of Africa south of the Sahara. Compared with the great volume of seasonal migrant labour in West Africa, the numbers of migrant agricultural labourers and of migrant workers to mineral and industrial enterprises are small.

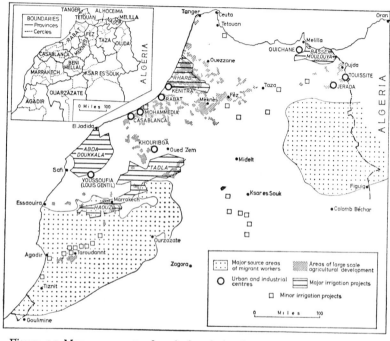

Figure 24 Morocco: areas of agricultural development, irrigation projects, urban and industrial centres, source areas of migrant labour for mining and industry. (Based in part on maps in *Atlas du Maroc*, Rabat.) Inset map: Administrative boundaries.

Nonetheless they may still play some part in the transmission of malaria, and could prejudice measures for eradication.

Movements of agricultural workers are governed by seasonal labour requirements, and though it is possible to define with some accuracy the places where labourers find work little is known of the areas from which they originate. The main demands for labour are in the areas of most advanced agricultural development, which are those lands which are either still farmed by Europeans or which have been appropriated recently by Moroccans and continue to be farmed by efficient modern methods. They total about 1,750,000 acres, representing about fifteen per cent of the total cultivated land in Morocco, and they include the areas where major irrigation works have been established (Figure 24). Some of the best developed unirrigated land is on the plains of Meknès and Fès, where cereal farming is mechanized and labour requirements are consequently low, though hand labour is required on the large acreages devoted to viticulture and citrus and other kinds of fruit-growing.

Labourers migrate from the poor highland areas to work in the irrigated lands along the foot of the High Atlas, and to the more extensive irrigated zones in the Rharb and Doukkala, and many of these major irrigated areas, like those near Beni Mellal, are probably malarious. The migrants come from altitudes where malaria is either absent or where the transmission season is very short. They are therefore highly susceptible to the disease like the migrants from Rwanda and Burundi in East Africa and suffer severe infections. Besides the major zones of irrigation in Morocco there are numerous minor projects and the plans for economic development in the future provide for a further increase in their number. By providing suitable conditions for mosquito breeding all the irrigated areas are potentially foci of malaria infection and will need particular attention to be paid to them in the malaria eradication programme. Measures will have to be taken both to reduce and, if possible, eliminate vector breeding, and to protect migrant elements from non-malarious areas who come to work in them.

There was formerly a seasonal movement of agricultural workers from parts of eastern Morocco (e.g. the Moulouya valley) to Algeria, but this almost ceased during the period of political, social and economic upheaval there between 1954 and 1962. If with the return to more settled conditions in Algeria it was to develop again, it would need to be watched very carefully if a malaria eradication programme was in progress in Morocco, but with no comparable work being undertaken in Algeria. Without effective control measures these labourers could return to Morocco with fresh infections. The return of this former movement is however unlikely since economic developments in recent years have provided more opportunities for work in Morocco; changes in land holding in Algeria with the acquisition of former French farms will reduce demands for labour, and the strained relations between Morocco and Algeria are likely to make Moroccans less acceptable.

Although it is possible only to generalize about agricultural labour more specific information is available on the movements of labourers to areas of mineral exploitation and industrial development in Morocco.

They come particularly from the mountains in the south-west of the country, from some areas of the plains and plateaux in the west, from the eastern parts of the Rif mountains, and from the high plateaux of eastern Morocco (Figure 24). The first and the last of these are the main source areas of migrant labour. Some of the movements have developed spontaneously in response to population pressure, land hunger and poverty, but workers are also recruited, as for example from among the Berbers from the south-west whose reputation for work is high. Recruiting tends to take place in particular areas for particular employment – workers in the coal-mines at Jerada come especially from the Anti-Atlas, and those in the phosphate mines at Khourigba from the plain of Tiznit south of Agadir and from the country around Bou-Izakarn. In eastern Morocco the infertile soils of the high plateaux and overpopulation in the eastern Rif provide impetus for movements to Jerada, Bou-Bkere, Touissite and Bou Arfa. Some tribes have more of their members involved in these movements than do others. The Beni Guil, traditionally a tribe of nomadic pastoralists, now also provide migrant labourers, and multiple mobility of this kind is likely to complicate further the influence of movements on malaria eradication.

While the main movements of industrial migrant labour are to the Khourigba–Louis Gentil and to the Oujda regions of mineral exploitation there are also more localized movements on a smaller scale to less important mining areas, especially in Ouarzazate and Tafilalet Provinces in southern Morocco. Because they are localized they are likely to provide little trouble for malaria eradication. In any case the total labour force employed in all mining activities in Morocco in 1960 was only 36,000 and all of these workers were not migrants. Though the total number involved is small, there is nonetheless a great deal of coming and going of labourers since turnover rates are high as in other developing countries. Only a small proportion of the labour force in any enterprise is stable and turnover may exceed seventy-five per cent per annum. This instability is linked with the very strong attachments that most migrant labourers feel for their homes in the rural areas, for the majority of them are only first-generation industrial workers and they are not prepared, for both social and economic reasons, to make a complete break with their traditional ways of life. There is a trend towards greater stability, and whereas the labour force of the Office Cherifien des Phosphates, the largest individual employer in Morocco, changed more than twice each year during the 1920s this had dropped to once a year during the 1940s and the rate is now less.

However, even with this trend, labour migration will continue for some time to come, and certainly throughout the period that a malaria eradication programme is likely to be operating. Since the malarious and non-malarious areas in Morocco have not yet been defined in detail it is impossible to be specific about the part that migrant labourers, both agricultural and industrial, may play in maintaining and spreading infection. Agricultural labourers are potentially the greater menace because they number more than the industrial workers and much less is known of their movements. A more thorough and complete check should be possible at all stages on migrant workers to mines and industries, to treat them for malaria and protect them against infection. It should also be possible to apply malaria eradication measures more thoroughly and more completely in the relatively restricted areas of mining and industrial development, than in the more extensive and more widely scattered lands with well-developed agriculture.

The exode rurale

The drift of population on a large scale from the countryside to settle permanently in the towns has been a feature in the past of countries like those in Western Europe which now have well developed economies in which industrialization is important. It is characteristic at the present day of developing countries in Africa and elsewhere in the world. In Morocco people are moving from those parts of the country which lie south and east of a line from Tetouan to El Jadida – particularly from the plains of Doukkala and Sgharna, from the plateaux which front the mountains of the Rif and the High Atlas, from the valley of the Dra, from Tafilalet and from the oasis of Figuig in the south-east. Rural poverty and the apparent attractions and amenities that urban life has to offer are the main factors which influence this rural exodus.

Poverty in the rural areas is caused not only by the severe limitations of the physical environment, but also by the rapid growth of population which has not yet been matched by a comparable development of the resources which are immediately available. One of the highest rates of rural depopulation between 1936 to 1952 was in fact from Doukkala, one of the better-watered parts of Morocco, but a region with one of the highest rates of population increase and with very limited economic development during that period. The population of Morocco was 11,626,000 in 1960, 2,316,000 more than that in 1952, and it is increasing at a rate in excess of two per cent per annum which was the figure used in drawing up the plans for economic development for the period 1960–64.

Figures in Table 9 show that though the rate of movements from the countryside has declined during the last inter-censal period the numbers

Table 9   The annual increase in rural population and the annual volume of rural exodus, 1936–52 and 1952–60.

Period	Total annual increase of rural population	Annual volume of rural exodus
1936–52	90,000	30,000
1952–60	220,000	40–50,000

Source: D. Noin, *L'Information Géographique*, **26**, 1962, 1

leaving have increased considerably. It was estimated that between 1955 and 1970 the natural increase of population in the rural areas would be 1,750,000, of whom about 700,000 would leave for the towns; the data from the 1960 census suggest that these figures have been underestimated. Such miscalculations are not unusual and are understandable in countries where there is a lack of reliable demographic data, where it is difficult to conduct accurate censuses and where there is a dearth of vital statistics.

The most striking feature of the rural exodus is the concentration of emigrants in the Atlantic coastal zone, and particularly in the towns of Casablanca, Rabat-Salé and Kenitra. Casablanca, the major commercial and industrial centre and port of Morocco, is far and away the greatest attraction and more than half of the emigrants from the rural areas of Morocco went there in the period 1952–60. Its population of nearly 1 million represents only a little less than ten per cent of the total population of Morocco. Rabat (227,445) and Kenitra (86,775) are much smaller and their rates of growth have been less. Other towns in Morocco have increased in size in the period from 1952–60, but to nothing like the same extent as these three. The rural areas immediately adjacent to these towns are also being settled by emigrants from the more remote parts of Morocco and they too show increasing populations.

Though the prospect of economic gain is one of the factors promoting the exodus of rural population the sources of employment in the towns are in fact insufficient to absorb all the immigrants and there is both urban unemployment and underemployment. There are also chronic shortages of housing. As a result of these shortages shanty towns, *bidonvilles*, have grown up on the outskirts of many of the big towns; these are built of whatever materials their inhabitants have been able to collect together – wood, cardboard, corrugated iron, sacking and the flattened petrol drums from which they get their name. They are completely unplanned and quite insanitary, without sewage and waste disposal and with water supplies that are totally inadequate for the demands made on them. The largest *bidonvilles* are around Casablanca and they shelter nearly a half of the population of the city; that of Beni M'Sik alone houses more than 50,000 people.

The densities of population in the *bidonvilles* vary considerably, averaging about 2,000 persons per acre, though densities are even higher in the *medinas*, the original nucleii of Moroccan towns to which modern urban growths have been added. Densities in the *medinas* of Fès, Rabat-Salé and Meknès are between 2,500 and 3,000 persons per acre and overcrowding is appalling. They are closely built up and the congested buildings and narrow airless alleyways are in fact more favourable breeding grounds for disease and infection than the impermanent ramshackle *bidonvilles* through which at least the air circulates freely. It is not surprising that a disease like tuberculosis flourishes among the inhabitants of the *medinas*.

Most of the exodus of population from the countryside to the towns is permanent. In the urban environment new social groupings develop; men are accompanied by their immediate dependents only and the conjugal family replaces the extended patriarchal family, which is traditional in both the Berber and Arab rural areas of Morocco. Related conjugal families may contrive to live close to one another in the towns in which they have settled and they may maintain some contacts with their home areas, but there is not the frequency of movement between them and the towns that there is with migrant labourers between their homes and the places to which they go to work. These infrequent movements are unlikely to present much difficulty for malaria eradication. But the malaria problems that may have to be dealt with among people resident in towns, and particularly in the *bidonvilles*, are likely to be very different from those encountered elsewhere in Morocco and a special study of the epidemiology of malaria in urban areas is necessary.

Of the various forms of population mobility in Morocco, those associated with nomadic pastoralism and with transhumance are declining and will continue to do so, while labour migration and particularly the rural exodus are becoming more important. Though these changes are taking place slowly they are likely to decrease the problems of mobility in a programme for malaria eradication. More investigation of agricultural labour migration is needed before its likely effects can be appreciated. Circumstances give no grounds for complacency but altogether population mobility in Morocco should present problems that are of much smaller magnitude as compared with those that have to be faced in

Africa south of the Sahara. The numbers of people involved are not as great, there is already a much larger body of information available on the various movements that take place, and there are better means available for obtaining more. The programme for malaria eradication is to be integrated with the existing and developing infrastructure of a countrywide medical and health service. *Aides-sanitaires* are being trained to collect basic geographical data on population distribution, settlement patterns and house types, and provision is being made for continuing revision of these to keep pace with changes. Further provision needs to be made for the collection of data on population mobility, but altogether the Moroccan arrangements are far in advance of those existing in other parts of Africa.

In Morocco the medical and health service has been built up and arranged with emphasis on the Province as the important unit in the organization. In charge of each province there is a *Médecin-Chef* who is able to exercise considerable independent control. As a result there is a tendency among the *Médecin-chefs* to think largely in provincial terms and to fail to relate conditions in their own province to those in adjacent provinces and in the country as a whole. These isolationist attitudes would be disastrous in executing a malaria eradication programme, especially when several types of population mobility involve the crossing and recrossing of provincial boundaries. Provinces must not be regarded as entities in themselves and their relationships with each other and with the country as a whole must be kept constantly in mind. If malaria eradication is to succeed it is essential for the work at all stages, in planning and in prosecution, to go forward for the country as a whole. This concept may be extended to the problems that may develop along Morocco's international boundaries. The need for cooperation, and, if possible, coordination with adjacent countries in planning malaria eradication has already been stressed. While considerable success should be possible in a Moroccan campaign for eradication, completely satisfactory results will only be achieved when malaria eradication can be planned and carried out for the whole of the Maghreb.

BIBLIOGRAPHY

The relevant literature is entirely in French. For essential background information on the country: J. Despois, *L'Afrique du Nord*, Paris, 1958;

J. Célérier, *Le Maroc*, Paris, 1953 and J. Miège, *Le Maroc*, Paris, 1962. Information on malaria may be found in *Initiation à la Pathologie Marocaine*, Rabat, 1955 and 'Projet du Plan d'Operations pour la Phase de Pre-Eradication du Paludisme au Maroc' 1962, Ministère de la Santé Publique, Rabat (unpublished). Some analyses of the 1960 census are in D. Noin, 'La Population du Maroc', *L'Information Géographique*, **26**, 1962, 1. Features of nomadic groups are discussed in V. Monteil, *Notes sur les Tekna*, 1948, and R. Paskoff, 'La Region de Berguent', *Cahiers d'Outre-Mer*, **10**, 1957, 34. J. Dresch, *Documents sur les Genres de Vie de Montagne dans le Massif Central du Grand Atlas*, Tours, 1941, is a classic study of transhumance; more recent aspects of this form of pastoralism are considered in R. Raynal, 'La Terre et l'Homme en Haut-Moulouya', *Bulletin Économique et Social du Maroc*, 1960. Details on migrant labour to mines and industries are given in J-P. Trystram, *L'Ouvrier Mineur au Maroc*, Paris, 1957 and in A. André and J. le Coz, *Atlas du Maroc*, planche 41, 'Economie Minière', Rabat, 1961; and on the 'exode rurale' in A. Adam, 'Problemes Sociaux du Maroc: l'Exode Rurale', *Sessions d'Études Juridiques, Politiques et Economiques* (Faculté du Droit du Maroc), **4**, 1959, 67.

This chapter is based on the following by the author: 'Rapport sur une visite au Maroc, July–September 1962', W.H.O. Regional Office for Europe (unpublished) and, 'Geographical Factors and Malaria Eradiation: the Case of Morocco', *Pacific Viewpoint*, **5**, 1964, 183.

9 Proposals and prospects

THE various examples in the preceding chapters, illustrating how geographical factors in Africa, particularly those associated with population mobility, influence malaria and its eradication, are neither atypical nor unrepresentative. Similar ones might be instanced from other parts of the continent and from other parts of the world where conditions are comparable. However much of a problem they may present for malaria eradication, these movements are a feature of life which cannot be changed in a short time. Though many of them are now undesirable, from many other points of view besides that of malaria eradication, they all developed in the first instance for reasons that were inevitable. Some evidence has been given of the ways in which the patterns and characters of movements are altering. These changes are taking place slowly, and where they are happening without upheaval and disturbance they are part of evolutionary processes to new ways of life. Attempts to push them ahead at any greater pace might only prove abortive. The fact has therefore to be faced that the rates of change are too slow to be of significance for malaria eradication, in terms of the timetables envisaged for its progress. Schemes for malaria eradication in Africa will therefore have to be adjusted to the population movements which are going on at the present time and they must be planned to accord with these movements and with other geographical factors. Much more needs to be known about population mobility, population distribution, settlement patterns, types of dwellings, farming practices, communications and water supply, and these are only the most important. They require investigation in much greater detail, similar to the malariological and entomological investigations that are regarded as essential in the work of malaria eradication.

Geographical conditions in any area are special and generalizations based on experience from only one area may be very dangerous. The physical environment in Africa often gives the appearance of uniformity over vast areas of the continent but this is an assumption which detailed studies show to be false. Rainfall and moisture conditions, which are important factors in vector breeding, may vary significantly over distances of only a few miles, not only in the amount of rainfall but in its incidence and reliability. Generalizations about people in Africa are also misleading; traditional groups of clans, tribes, chiefdoms and kingdoms into which people were divided in the past remain important at the present day, even with the growth of nationalism and the emergence of independent states. Social relationships, economic activities and religious and other beliefs vary enormously between these groups, and though common origins and contacts may have produced some common traits the individuality of each group is of paramount importance.

While detailed investigations of the physical environment and of

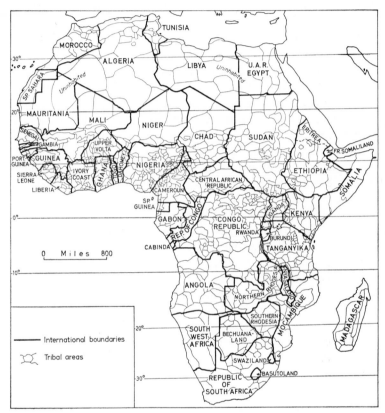

Figure 25 Major tribal areas in Africa. (Based on information in G. P. Murdock, *Africa: its People and their Culture History*, 1959.)

human circumstances are vital it is also important for comparative purposes to be able to view them in a wider context. Such an overall view permits a better appreciation of what may be encountered in terms of variety and difference between one area and another. With these in mind a series of maps have been prepared which show the distribution in Africa of several human factors relevant to malaria eradication. The first of these (Figure 25) illustrates the complexity of tribal groupings and the very high degree of ethnic fragmentation in some parts of Africa, for example in eastern Nigeria and adjacent parts of Cameroon and on the Nile–Congo watershed. In fact this map is a simplification of the actual situation which is even more complex and could not be shown on a scale suitable for the whole continent. Furthermore, tribal groups do not in fact occupy well-defined areas that are ethnically homogeneous and which can be delimited by rigid boundaries. Past and present population movements have been responsible for a continuous mixing together of peoples. Though a particular ethnic group may predominate in an area there are likely to be minority groups there also. Though minority groups may number only a few people they will still maintain certain characteristics in their ways of life which distinguish them from one another and from the main group.

International boundaries frequently divide tribal groups, and where people of the same group live on either side of a boundary there will inevitably be considerable movement backwards and forwards across it. The relevance of such movements to schemes for malaria eradication which are based on national territories has already been discussed, and official and unofficial attitudes to boundaries at the present day are important. When these boundaries delimited colonial territories they were regarded by Africans as the unwanted creations of the European powers. The anomalies and inconsistencies associated with them were continually, and quite rightly, criticized. Now that the majority of the colonial territories are independent states with the same boundaries which were formerly criticized, the governments of these states have shown great reluctance to consider any changes in them. Where there are major boundary problems, as for example between Ethiopia and Somalia, Ghana and Togo, Algeria and Morocco, the prospects of revision seem very slight. Inevitably these problems engender poor relations between the countries concerned and thus reduce the likelihood of achieving effective cooperation in malaria eradication and in other fields of development.

Where movements of population cross not one but several international boundaries there are two possible ways of dealing with the problems which they create for malaria eradication. The first would be for these boundaries to be effectively sealed, either to prevent movements across them or to ensure that they are strictly controlled. There has been no evidence to show that this is possible in Africa. During the Second World War an attempt was made to close the land boundary between British and French Somaliland to complement a sea blockade of the port of Djibouti. Though the boundary was only eighty miles long, and the attempt to close it was organized as a military operation with severe penalties imposed on anyone trying to break through, effective control could not be maintained and movements between the two countries continued to take place. Similarly the official closures of the boundaries between the Gold Coast and adjacent French territories in West Africa in 1941–43 failed to prevent movements across them.

Recently it was reported that Pakistan, by using its military forces for control, had effectively sealed its boundaries to prevent the incursion of nomads from Afghanistan, but these measures were successful in terrain where the routes available for movement are restricted. Across the majority of boundaries in Africa there are few natural restrictions to movement, and if nothing less than a military operation is necessary to exercise control then there is no country in Africa at present, with the possible exception of South Africa, with forces large enough to mount one. If, in the future, the boundaries of African states assume even greater political sanctity, movements between one country and another may become less free and more controlled than they were under European government. It may well be possible for independent African governments to introduce such measures and for them to be acceptable to their peoples, whereas they would have been regarded as repressive impositions if they had been instituted under colonial rule. Even so, the introduction of measures is not enough; they become effective only if they can be enforced.

If boundary control is impossible, or is likely to become effective only in the distant future, an alternative way of dealing with interterritorial movements will be to establish interterritorial malaria eradication projects. Only a limited start has been made in this direction, with one project involving parts of Southern Rhodesia, Moçambique and South Africa and another Cameroon, Nigeria, Dahomey and Togo. How effective these are will not be known for some time, but it is probable that they will still not contain all movements of population within their limits. Attention has been drawn earlier in this book to the movement of people that takes place between Northern Nigeria and Ghana and which passes through Dahomey and Togo. It will probably be necessary to enlarge the area of these projects in order to meet such circumstances, in the same way as pilot eradication projects were enlarged in an attempt to contain movements of population. To solve the problem entirely a simultaneous malaria eradication programme would need to be devised for the whole of Africa. For many reasons this is impracticable, but it should be possible to delimit major regions in the continent each of which would circumscribe a group of population movements, and then mount schemes for eradication successively in each region.

Figures 26, 27 and 28 provide a continental view of the distribution of three other geographical factors that are particularly relevant to malaria eradication. Broad distinctions in the types of subsistence economies, settlement patterns and dwellings have been indicated, but with detailed field investigation it would be possible to develop further subdivisions and combinations of these.

For subsistence economies the basic distinctions are between crop cultivation and pastoralism, and between sedentary and nomadic (and transhumance) ways of life. Other economies, such as hunting and collecting, fishing and oasis cultivation, are recognized separately though they are practised by relatively few people. From roughly

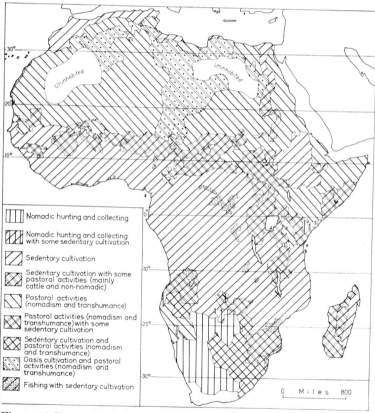

Figure 26 Types of subsistence agriculture in Africa. (Based on Murdock, *op. cit.*)

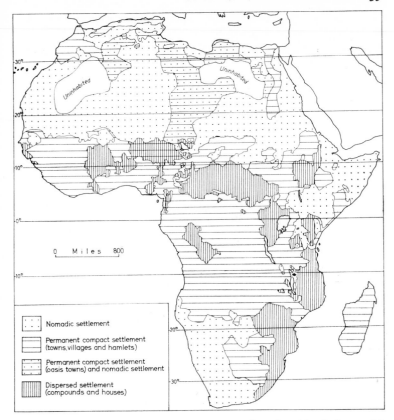

Figure 27 Types of settlement pattern in Africa. (Based on Murdock, *op. cit.*)

latitudes 10° N to 10° S sedentary crop cultivation is the basis of the economies of the majority of tribal groups, but with the form that it takes varying in respect both of the crops grown and the methods of cultivation used. These variations are dependent on factors of the physical environment and of social and economic organization. Modifications in subsistence economies resulting from the development of cash crops, and in some instances the introduction of new crops, have not been shown; they are particularly important in West Africa. Areas in North, East, Central and South Africa which have been settled and developed by European farmers are not shown either, nor are those areas where there has been a complete change from agriculture to other forms of economic activity. These modifications and changes, which have come about in the present century, directly affect only limited parts of the

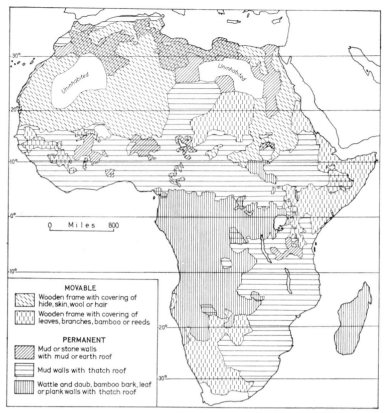

Figure 28. Types of dwelling in Africa. (Based on Murdock, *op. cit.*)

continent, but their effect on the development of migrant labour has been indicated already.

Sufficient has been said of the influence of settlement and dwellings on malaria eradication to make apparent the relevance of these distributions and little comment on them is necessary. Only the predominant pattern of settlement has been indicated and there are probably few areas in Africa where any one pattern is exclusive. Areas with predominantly dispersed settlement have occasional nucleated settlements, usually small towns which function as administrative and commercial centres, and these are also found in areas with predominantly nomadic settlement. Only indigenous African settlement patterns and types of dwellings have been mapped, and though these have been modified by external influences in particular areas the modifications affect the general situation to only a limited extent.

The influences of geographical factors on malaria eradication, to which attention has been directed in this book, have been emphasized in almost all the reports of the W.H.O. Expert Committee on Malaria. This committee, whose members are malariologists of international eminence, meets at intervals of about two years to review developments in malariology and the progress of eradication, and to recommend lines of approach for future work. In 1960 it reviewed at some length the factors which had been responsible for malaria eradication projects failing to achieve the success that had been hoped for. Under the heading of *technical failures*, the lack of appreciation of the importance of human habits and socio-economic conditions were listed, with population mobility as the factor that was most frequently the cause of failure. *Operational failures* included 'deficient geographical reconnaissance' which resulted in 'deficient coverage in spraying operations', and 'difficulties in communications' due to faulty or inadequate information on transport and its problems in project areas.

Geographical reconnaissance has progressively come to be regarded as an essential element in malaria eradication. Some of the data required are readily available for areas where eradication is being planned, but for the most part this is uncommon. The major malarious areas of the world are deficient in most kinds of data, or else these are so superficial as to be useless. It is essential to ensure that all available information is brought together and checked, and those responsible for geographical reconnaissance in malaria eradication should be in close contact with the various technical services in the countries in which they are working, in the likely event that they may be able to supply some of the information required on such things as agriculture, irrigation, water supply, trade and communications.

There may be no data of the kinds required and data are always likely to require supplementing and bringing up to date; the last is especially necessary when they relate to human conditions which are highly dynamic and constantly changing. Geographical reconnaissance must be organized so that changes can be observed and earlier plans can then be modified to take them into account. It needs to be a continuing feature in the eradication programme, flexible and capable of being adapted to meet any circumstances that arise. If geographical reconnaissance is to be adequate it must count equal in importance with investigations carried out on malaria parasites and mosquitoes.

Failure to analyse and evaluate geographical data adequately is due to lack of training and to the lack of time available to undertake this work on the part of those members of malaria eradication teams who are responsible for geographical reconnaissance. Malaria eradication teams have no member who is specifically concerned with geographical reconnaissance and is adequately trained for it. Thus, while the medical aspects of malaria are investigated by a fully-trained and experienced malariologist, and the mosquito vectors are studied by a specialist entomologist, no specialist is assigned to the collection, analysis and evaluation of data on vital geographical, and particularly human, factors.

The need for geographical reconnaissance has been generally recognized but the means for undertaking it are inadequate, and until these are provided geographical factors will not receive the attention that they require. They will continue to prejudice eradication projects in the various ways that have been illustrated in this book and satisfactory solutions are unlikely to be found to the problems which they create. If persons were appointed specifically to undertake the tasks of geographical reconnaissance they would work in the closest association with malariologists and entomologists, to produce fully integrated assessments of the complex relationships between the three elements – parasites, mosquitoes and men – which produce malaria. At the present time inadequate consideration is being given to men and to the environments in which they live.

BIBLIOGRAPHY

G. P. Murdock, *Africa: its Peoples and their Culture History*, 1959, provides an excellent ethnographic survey of the continent in one volume, though some of its interpretations are open to question. More detailed information is provided by the monographs of the *Ethnographic Survey of Africa*, published by the International African Institute. See also, R. M. Prothero, 'African Ethnographic Maps, with a New Example from Northern Nigeria', *Africa*, 32, 1962, 61, and *Cartes Ethno-Démographiques de l'Afrique Occidentale*, published by the Institut Français d'Afrique Noire, Dakar. Boundaries and their problems are considered by K. M. Barbour, 'A Geographical Analysis of Boundaries in Inter-Tropical Africa', in Barbour and Prothero (*ed.*), *op. cit.*, 303. The reports of the Expert Committee on Malaria are published in the *World Health Organization Technical Report Series*.

Index